Psychobiological Approaches to Social Behavior

Psychobiological Approaches to Social Behavior

edited by
P. Herbert Leiderman and David Shapiro

Stanford University Press, Stanford, California   1964

Preface

This volume is an outgrowth of a symposium sponsored jointly by the Department of Psychiatry of the Harvard Medical School and the Office of Naval Research. The meeting was held on April 19 and 20, 1963, at the Holyoke Center, Harvard University. The purpose of the symposium was to bring together individuals whose experimental research on social and group behavior combined biological as well as psychological or sociological techniques and concepts.

We hope that this volume will stimulate further research on basic theoretical and methodological problems of the psychobiological approach, a relatively undeveloped and challenging area of experimentation. The book consists of nine papers based on presentations at the symposium, modified to suit the more formal requirements of publication. Besides the authors of these papers, Arthur Couch, Abraham Levine, George Mahl, Vincent Nowlis, Luigi Petrullo, Anatol Rapoport, Gilbert Tolhurst, and Richard Trumbull participated actively in the conference. We regret that the necessary limitations on the scope of the book excluded the papers of Couch, Mahl, Nowlis, and Rapoport. The introductory and final chapters incorporate many ideas discussed at the symposium, for which we are grateful to the participants.

We particularly want to thank Dr. Jack R. Ewalt of the Harvard Medical School, and Dr. Richard Trumbull, Mr. Luigi Petrullo, and Drs. Abraham Levine and Gilbert Tolhurst of the Office of Naval Research, whose efforts made the symposium possible. We would like to acknowledge major research support provided by Office of Naval

Research Contract Nonr-1866 (43), Group Psychology Branch, and the following grants from the U.S. Public Health Service National Institute of Mental Health: Career-Investigatorship Award M-2276 and Research Career Development Award K3-MH-20, 476-01.

For their assistance and encouragement, we are most thankful to our associates, Andrew Crider and Bernard Tursky, and to our secretaries, Marion R. Kaufmann and Catherine C. Hanley, all of the Harvard Medical School. We also wish to thank Miss Elaine Lasky of Stanford University Press, Miss Anne Jaeger, and Miss Stefanie Tashjian for their valued editorial assistance in bringing the book through to the final stages.

P. HERBERT LEIDERMAN
Stanford University School of Medicine
DAVID SHAPIRO
Harvard Medical School

Contents

Foreword

DAVID A. HAMBURG
Stanford University School of Medicine

This is an important book. It brings together many interesting data from a diversity of sources. Such data would usually be scattered through the literature of half a dozen traditional disciplines. Above all, the book, and the conference from which it grew, promotes interaction between the biological and social sciences.

There is much to be gained from such interaction. These fields are, after all, the group of sciences concerned with living organisms, and there are many points of contact, as this volume shows. The social sciences are, for the most part, fledglings on the scientific scene. Workers in fields such as psychology, anthropology, and sociology may well find it stimulating and encouraging to examine the experience of their older cousins in such fields as genetics, evolution, physiology, and ecology. After all, it was not so long ago that many respectable citizens, including some scientists, were saying that little progress could be expected in the biological sciences because living organisms did not, or should not, lend themselves to scientific analysis. This may sound familiar to scientific students of behavior. In any event, research on social aspects of behavior generally rests on some conceptions about the nature of the species whose aggregations are in focus, and these conceptions hopefully are informed by data. Surely these data, in the 1960's, cannot legitimately omit the fundamental advances of biology, so many of which are pertinent to human behavior and its disorders (Hamburg, 1962).

By the same token, any comprehensive human biology cannot legitimately omit one of man's most striking characteristics, his social nature. The biological research of recent years has brilliantly achieved an increasingly refined analysis of the parts of living organisms, including man, at the cellular, subcellular, and molecular levels (Korey, Pope, and Robins, 1962). At the same time, there has been considerable progress in clarifying the interdependence of the parts of the organism and their coordination in relation to environmental conditions (Nalbandov, 1963). Moreover, much has been gained by considering not only individuals but populations (Mayr, 1963; Etkin, 1964). Nevertheless, the systematic (and, where possible, experimental) study of social interaction and organization has received much less attention than it deserves in the biological sciences.

During the past few years, I have been greatly interested in observing the emergence of promising lines of inquiry at various points of contact between the biological and social sciences. I should like to mention briefly a few such lines of inquiry, the choice being purely idiosyncratic. My purpose is to indicate something of the diversity of the traditional disciplines drawn upon by such investigations, and something of the scope of possibilities in this kind of research. Some of my examples are chosen because they are not emphasized in the present volume.

Let me begin with an area that is well represented in the present volume, for example in the research of the editors: physiological responses to group situations. Social factors in small group interaction have been shown to influence the galvanic skin potential (Leiderman and Shapiro, 1964), plasma-free fatty acids (Bogdonoff et al., 1962), and urinary excretion of 17-hydroxycorticosteroids (Fishman et al., 1962). From these leads, it seems altogether likely that CNS-mediated changes in a variety of endocrine and autonomic functions will be discovered in the next few years under conditions of strong affect engendered in group situations. Indeed, it appears that small groups may emerge as one of the most potent experimental tools in human stress research. So far, the groups utilized in such studies have largely been groups of strangers, brought together on an ad hoc basis for one or a few brief encounters. In view of the strong emotional responses regularly occurring in family diagnostic and therapeutic sessions (Minuchin et al.,1964), it is surprising that such situations have so far had virtually no utilization in psychobiological research. On the basis of such clinical observations, it seems reasonable to expect that strong affect might be dependably and legitimately aroused in situations involving family discussions of a joint problem; concomitant measurement of endocrine and autonomic variables should prove rewarding. The application of techniques of telemetry should further enhance our ability to measure physiological concomitants of naturally occurring group situations (Slater, 1963).

This brings to mind a related area of investigation involving a combination of ecological and physiological techniques in an effort to clarify some stress phenomena in small mammals. A number of studies in recent years have been concerned with the relations of population density, endocrine function, and behavior. In investigations with a variety of small mammalian species, involving both laboratory and field studies, evidence has emerged suggesting that as population density increases to high levels, adrenal function tends to increase considerably and gonadal function diminishes; moreover, such increases in population density are, in many species, associated with a striking tendency toward aggressive behavior (Thiessen, 1964; Mayer and Van Gelder, 1963). There are also some intriguing observations suggesting the possibility of increased susceptibility to a variety of diseases under conditions of high population density (Christian, 1961; Ratcliffe and Cronin, 1958). There is some evidence that effects of increasing population density are considerably influenced by the genotype and the prior experience of the animals. Most of these investigations have a tantalizing quality. They deal with important phenomena and point in stimulating directions for future research; but for the most part the crucial data are not yet available.

In a similar vein, it was discovered a few years ago that crowding significantly increases the toxicity of various sympathomimetic amines, especially amphetamine, in mice. Further experiments showed that phenobarbital, chlorpromazine, and reserpine afford definite protection to such grouped animals (Lasagna and McCann, 1957). This has now been confirmed in several laboratories. There are indications that a variety of adrenergic blocking agents protect mice against the crowding effect to a substantial extent, whereas monoamine oxidase inhibitors may increase the crowding effect. At present, investigations are under way in an effort to elucidate the biochemical mechanism of such effects (Lal and Chessick, 1964).

The intimate integration of social and biological factors is perhaps nowhere better illustrated than in recent research on human evolution (Washburn, 1963; Howell and Bourlière, 1963; Dobzhansky, 1962). The past few years have seen a remarkable upsurge in careful, systematic studies of the behavior of the most complex nonhuman primates under natural conditions (Devore, in press), and of those few remaining hunting-and-gathering human societies that have been largely unaffected by modern technology and its "civilized" bearers. These studies, along with remarkable discoveries in prehistoric archaeology and paleontology pertaining to the earliest men, are now providing a much more adequate basis for the understanding of human evolution than we have ever had before. One major aspect of these investigations deserves mention here, because, in my judgment, it provides a fundamental link between social and biological processes. In brief, the newer studies strongly support the concept that in primate evolution, social organization has functioned as biological adaptation (Hamburg, 1963). The field observations of both nonhuman primates and hunting-and-gathering societies suggest that group living has conferred a powerful selective advantage upon more highly developed primates. This selective advantage has probably included protection against predation, the meeting of nutritional requirements, protection against climatic variation, coping with injuries, facilitating reproduction, and preparing the young to meet the requirements and exploit the opportunities of a given environment, whatever its characteristics may be. It is perhaps not too much to suggest that the extraordinary adaptive radiation of Homo sapiens, which is one of the most striking facts of evolutionary biology, has been heavily dependent upon human social organization.

In the field studies of nonhuman primates under natural conditions, one of the most striking and consistent observations has been the extraordinary richness and diversity of interanimal contact during the years of growth and development. Recent laboratory investigations with primate species have provided a stark and informative contrast. The most dramatic comparison is provided by the social isolation experiments (Harlow and Harlow, 1965; Mason and Sponholz, 1963). The behavioral effects of raising monkeys (Rhesus Macaque) until early adolescence in total social isolation—including isolation from contact both with other monkeys and with man—have proved quite devastating. The effects include: (1) gross disruption of interanimal contact, with emphasis on withdrawal and avoidance of contact; (2) crouching for long periods with very few responses directed toward the environment; (3) a variety of maladaptive, self-oriented behavior patterns, including persistent thumbsucking, self-clasping, and stereotyped rocking; (4) self-punitive behavior, such as biting the forearm, particularly on approach of other animals. The effects of partial social isolation are similar, though less profound and somewhat more reversible. Current research in this area involves, among other things, an attempt to determine the minimum length of time of rearing in social isolation that will produce these profound effects; an extension of such work to chimpanzees; and an attempt to determine whether adrenal function is permanently affected by such abnormal early experiences. The last is particularly interesting in the light of recent research with small mammals showing that environmental stimulation in infancy may have a permanent effect on adrenocortical responses to stress (Levine, 1962).

Another interesting development in social-biological research is that epidemiologic studies of cardiovascular and other diseases have recently begun to take more adequate account of social variables (Geiger and Scotch, 1963; Scotch and Geiger, 1963). Several other examples could be cited, but enough has perhaps been said to suggest the potential importance of this sort of research. The editors and contributors to this volume have provided a stimulating sample of research in an area of great promise. This area has been something less than fashionable, and its opportunities have only begun to be exploited. Research along the lines described here might usefully occupy many talented young people for years to come. I hope such people will give this volume the thoughtful reading it deserves.

References

Bogdonoff, M., Back, K., Klein, R., Estes, E., and Nichols, C. The physiologic response to conformity pressure in man. *Ann. intern. Med.*, 1961, **23**, 23–32.

Christian, J. J. Phenomena associated with population density. *Proc. Nat. Acad. Sci.*, 1961, **47**, 428–49.

Devore, I. (Ed.). *Primate behavior, field studies of monkeys and apes.* New York: Holt, Rinehart, Winston (in press).

Dobzhansky, T. *Mankind evolving.* New Haven: Yale Univ. Press, 1962.

Etkin, W. (Ed.). *Social behavior and organization among vertebrates.* Chicago: Univ. Chicago Press, 1964.

Fishman, J., Hamburg, D., Handlon, J., Mason, J., and Sachar, E. Emotional and adrenal cortical responses to a new experience: effect of social environment. *Arch. gen. Psychiat.,* 1962, 6, 271–78.

Geiger, H. J., and Scotch, N. The epidemiology of essential hypertension. I. Biologic mechanisms and descriptive epidemiology. *J. chronic Dis.,* 1963, 16, 1151–82.

Hamburg, D. Recent advances in biological sciences pertinent to the study of human behavior. In Masserman, J. (Ed.), *Science and psychoanalysis.* New York: Grune and Stratton, 1962. Pp. 37–53.

Hamburg, D. Emotions in the perspective of human evolution. In Knapp, P. (Ed.), *Expression of the emotions in man.* New York: International Universities Press, 1963. Pp. 300–317.

Harlow, H., and Harlow, Margaret. The effect of rearing conditions on behavior. *Int. J. Psychiat.,* 1965, 1, 43–51.

Howell, F. C., and Bourlière, R. (Eds.). *African ecology and human evolution.* Chicago: Aldine, 1963.

Korey, S., Pope, A., and Robins, E. (Eds.). *Ultrastructure and metabolism of the nervous system.* Baltimore: Williams and Wilkins, 1962.

Lal, H., and Chessick, R. Biochemical mechanism of amphetamine toxicity in isolated and aggregated mice. *Life Sci.,* 1964, 3, 381–84.

Lasagna, L., and McCann, W. Effect of "tranquilizing" drugs on amphetamine toxicity in aggregated mice. *Science,* 1957, 125, 1241.

Leiderman, P. H., and Shapiro, D. Studies on the galvanic skin potential level: some behavioral correlates. *J. psychosom. Res.,* 1964, 7, 277–81.

Levine, S. Plasma free corticosteroid response to electric shock in rats stimulated in infancy. *Science,* 1962, 135, 795–96.

Mason, W., and Sponholz, R. Behavior of rhesus monkeys raised in isolation. *J. psychiat. Res.,* 1963, 1, 299–306.

Mayer, W. V., and Van Gelder, R. G. (Eds.). *Physiological mammalogy.* Vol. I. *Mammalian populations.* New York: Academic Press, 1963.

Mayr, E. *Animal species and evolution.* Cambridge: Harvard Univ. Press, 1963.

Minuchin, S., Auerswald, E., King, C., and Rabinowitz, C. The study and treatment of families that produce multiple acting-out boys. *Amer. J. Orthopsychiat.,* 1964, 34, 125–33.

Nalbandov, A. (Ed.). *Advances in neuroendocrinology.* Urbana: Univ. of Illinois Press, 1963.

Ratcliffe, H., and Cronin, M. Changing frequency of arteriosclerosis in mammals and birds at the Philadelphia Zoological Garden. *Circulation,* 1958, 18, 41–52.

Scotch, N., and Geiger, H. J. The epidemiology of essential hypertension. II. Psychologic and sociocultural factors in etiology. *J. chronic Dis.*, 1963, **16**, 1183–1213.

Slater, L. (Ed.). *Bio-telemetry: The use of telemetry in animal behavior and physiology in relation to ecological problems.* London: Pergamon, 1963.

Thiessen, D. Population density and behavior: a review of theoretical and physiological contributions. *Texas Rep. Biol. Med.*, 1964, **22**, 266–314.

Washburn, S. (Ed.). *Classification and human evolution.* Chicago: Aldine, 1963.

Psychobiological Approaches to Social Behavior

Introduction *by the Editors*

This volume brings together a number of papers that utilize social and biological concepts and techniques in the study of behavior and group interaction. These papers constitute an attempt to survey and delimit a relatively new area of research and to describe useful methods and define issues for systematic study in the future. They have in common the goal of integration of social and biological phenomena, though they differ in the use of research strategies and tactics. The possibility of a marriage of social and biological viewpoints and methods grows out of an expanding knowledge of interpersonal behavior, an increase in the interest of social and biological scientists in each other's problems and techniques, and the dissatisfaction of many with the limitations imposed by the narrow framework of a single specialized field.

The assumption that physiological functioning is influenced by social environment seems obvious, until it becomes clear that social psychological conditions in physiological investigations are rarely specified. We know, for example, that the type of instructions given a subject, the sex, status, and ethnic background of the experimenter, and the setting of the experimental situation are as important in determining physiological response as the ingestion of drugs and the state of physical health of the subject. The papers in this book take into account these and more general social phenomena in order to investigate systematically the influence of such psycho-social factors on bodily responses.

The combining of social and biological concepts and techniques derives from the recent development of reliable recording and data-

processing techniques, which allow continuous observation of behavioral and physiological responses. It also depends on the increasing sophistication of social psychological research techniques, which
bring social psychological phenomena into the laboratory setting.
The great improvement in automatic techniques of programming experimental stimuli and in recording physiological and behavioral activity allows the study of several subjects simultaneously, over relatively long periods of time, and makes it possible to manipulate social variables while continuously monitoring a number of physiological and behavioral functions. The resulting advance, then, is
largely due to the ability of the researcher to make concurrent observations of physiological responses and behavior in specified social and group contexts.

The possibilities that physiological techniques offer for increasing
the information obtained from social psychological experiments has
been illustrated in several ways in the papers in this volume. Physiological procedures have been used to assess the covert effects of various social environments and roles, to determine the efficacy of the
experimental induction of social and attitudinal variables, and to
assess the effects of social influences on behavior-induced illness and
affective states. They have also been used to determine individual
differences in response to social demands, to differentiate individual
patterns of response in different group settings, and to study affective
response and equilibrium in social interaction. On the other hand,
physiological states have been directly manipulated by the use of
drugs, and the resulting behavior under varying social conditions
has been evaluated. Thus, in the research reported in this volume,
both social and physiological variables have been manipulated, together and separately, and their relationship has been elucidated.

Although the research efforts are mainly directed toward human
behavior, comparative studies are included to emphasize the evolutionary significance of social behavior. The studies deal with the
effects of other individuals in varying relationships, the impact of
different conditions of success and failure in a social setting, the social facilitation of behavior and physiological responses, and the implications of the social condition for physiological functions.

The orientation of this research is empirical by necessity and experimental by choice. The empiricism may be attributed to the ab-

sence of systematic theory relating biological to social psychological events. The facts reported and the methods of analysis employed are preliminary inductive steps toward more general formulations. The experimental bias of the studies is an affirmation that social events, complex though they may be, can be the object of rigorous analysis through the careful specification of observational conditions and the manipulation and quantification of relevant variables.

To summarize, these studies attempt to demonstrate how physiological measurements can provide indices of individual response which are objective and which can be quantified while social and behavioral variables are being assessed. Not only does this approach free the experimenter from depending solely on subjective judgments, but it also enables him to time-lock social and physiological events by simultaneous measurement. As social and biological scientists become more familiar with each other's problems and methods, we anticipate that other kinds of applications and other kinds of integrations can be made.

The Sensitivity of Psychoendocrine Systems to Social and Physical Environment

JOHN W. MASON AND JOSEPH V. BRADY
Walter Reed Army Institute of Research

The psychobiological approach to be discussed in this chapter, a combined behavioral and neuroendocrinological approach, has been applied in our laboratory primarily to the experimental study of emotional and psychosomatic processes. Although a number of interesting incidental observations have suggested the possibility that this approach is relevant as well to the study of social behavior, it has apparently not yet been the focus of a systematic, long-term exploration by workers in the psychoendocrine field. This neglect may perhaps be sufficient justification for our including in this book an account of largely incidental and inconclusive findings that suggest the influence of social factors on psychoendocrine systems. We hope more generally, however, to make the experimentally strategic point that endocrine systems are remarkably sensitive to psychological and environmental influences which alter emotional state. The rationale might then be ventured that if psychoendocrine measurements are sensitive indices of emotional responses, and if emotional responses are important indicators of social interaction, then the psychoendocrine approach should be useful to the investigator of social behavior.

Recent studies suggest that it may also be possible to use this approach to investigate other aspects of behavior relevant to social interaction. In particular, this approach may illuminate a broad class of functions, such as psychological defenses and tension-relieving mechanisms, that serve to minimize or counteract emotional involvement. In the discussion that follows, we shall review a series of observations showing hormonal responses to environmental factors in both the rhesus monkey and man which appear to raise the question of relevance to the study of social behavior. It should be emphasized that many of these findings are from collaborative studies with other investigators and have been published previously in greater detail.

Our experiments have been based largely upon the measurement of plasma and urinary 17-hydroxycorticosteroid (17-OH-CS) levels as indices of pituitary–adrenal cortical activity. More limited studies have been made with plasma and urinary epinephrine and norepinephrine measurements as indices of sympathetic–adrenal medullary activity. While these two neuroendocrine systems have proven remarkably sensitive to psychological influences and remain probably the systems of choice for the detection of acute psychoendocrine disturbances, recent work in this field makes it clear that many, if not all, of the endocrine systems respond to some extent during emotional disturbances. It appears increasingly that the most meaningful dimension to consider is not the change in absolute levels of activity in any single endocrine system, however important it may be for survival or vigor, but rather the broader patterning or balance of secretory change in the many interdependent endocrine systems which in concert regulate metabolic events. Good evidence now indicates not only that points of articulation occur, largely in the brain stem, between nerve cells and the pituitary–adrenal system, but that anatomical connections do exist which afford psychological mechanisms potential access to a wide range of endocrine systems, including those involving the gonadal, thyroid, and posterior pituitary glands. Hence, as we consider data that deal primarily with 17-OH-CS changes, we should keep always in our minds that many other concurrent endocrine (and autonomic) changes are probably occurring and that an ultimate aim in this field must be to study as many of these together as possible if we are to gain fuller insight into the operation of the central integrating mechanisms.

Social Influences on Basal Levels of 17-Hydroxycorticosteroids

Our first observations that suggested the sensitivity of the pituitary–adrenal cortical system to environmental influences occurred in the course of collecting normative data in the monkey. A few weeks before our own cage facilities for monkeys were ready for use, we ob-

tained morning and afternoon blood samples on five adult monkeys
housed in a large community cage in the central veterinary unit.

Table 1 shows the plasma 17-OH-CS levels of the monkeys housed
in groups compared with the values obtained on similar animals from
the same compound after they were housed individually in separate
cages for several weeks in our own unit. Not only is the mean 9 A.M.
level of 51 µg % of the group-housed animals high by comparison
with the level of this morning control group, 38 µg %, but over the
years we have found normal 9 A.M. plasma 17-OH-CS levels to average about 30 µg % in the basal, normal, individually housed monkey.
Note the slight downward trend of 17-OH-CS levels in the afternoon
for monkeys in individual cages, which represents the very consistent
diurnal variation in this neuroendocrine system (Mason, 1959).
Many similar observations have been reported by other investigators
in both laboratory and field studies relating hypertrophy of the adrenal gland to population density in animals (Christian, 1961; Thiessen
and Rodgers, 1961).

TABLE 1

*Comparison of Plasma 17-OH-CS Levels in Monkeys Housed in
Community and in Individual Cages*

Time	Community cages $(N = 5)$	Individual cages $(N = 10)$
9 A.M.	51	38
3 P.M.	51	26

A second related observation that suggests a reflection of social interaction in corticosteroid levels was made in animals housed for a
while in closed cages, separated visually from their neighbors, and
then moved into wire mesh cages where visual and tactile contact occurred with adjacent animals.

Table 2 shows mean values of two or more diurnal plasma 17-OH-
CS measurements in each of three monkeys, first in room A and later
in room B. In all instances levels are greater in room B than in room
A. The differences are not very great, although the direction of change
is very consistent. Room A was a quiet room in which a few monkeys
were kept individually in solid sheet-metal cages open only in the
front. Room B was a monkey colony in which about 20 to 30 monkeys
were kept individually in open mesh cages with relatively free inter-

TABLE 2

Basal Plasma 17-OH-CS Levels in Same Monkeys Housed in
Two Different Rooms

Subject and time		Room A	Room B
M-1	9 A.M.	23	34
	3 P.M.	16	27
M-2	9 A.M.	28	34
	3 P.M.	19	23
M-3	9 A.M.	32	38
	3 P.M.	23	31
Mean	9 A.M.	28	35
	3 P.M.	19	27

action between adjacent animals. The fact that levels were lower in the first room than in the second perhaps militates against an explanation of simple adaptation to caging with time; nevertheless we cannot conclude, but can only suggest, that a social factor was reflected in these experiments (Mason, 1959).

Another observation along this line was made in monkeys placed in a restraining chair, which has been used extensively for primate studies by many workers (Mason, 1959). Both extremities are free, the animal feeds itself, and urinary samples as well as blood samples may be readily obtained. Initially the only space available for the study of animals restrained in this way was in the corner of our biochemistry laboratory where routine 17-OH-CS determinations were being made. As we started to obtain normal urinary 17-OH-CS excretion data to go with our plasma data, the following interesting observation was made.

Figure 1* shows mean urinary 17-OH-CS excretion by the day of the week and represents a total of 50 measurements in five monkeys. During the working week when two chemists, as well as the monkeys, occupied the room, levels ran about 1.9 to 1.5 mg per day, highest on Monday. On the quiet weekend, however, levels dropped about 30 per cent. Again, interaction with other organisms seems the most plausible explanation, but the experiment does not conclusively rule out all other factors (Mason, 1959). It is interesting that a similar effect has

* Figures 1 through 5 are U.S. Army photographs.

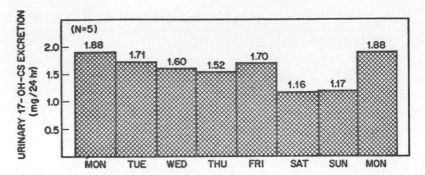

FIG. 1. Variations in mean urinary 17-OH-CS excretion during the
week in monkeys adapted to the chair.

been observed in a human subject, a patient hospitalized for elective
surgery for bronchiectasis, who was studied through a long pre-opera-
tive period of diagnostic evaluation.

Figure 2 shows a series of successive daily urinary 17-OH-CS measurements in this patient, which show a clear drop on Saturday and
Sunday compared with weekdays. No special studies were conducted
on the patient himself during this period, but he was confined to a
thoracic surgery ward that bustled with activity during the weekdays
when surgery and admissions occurred. On the weekends the patient
retired to the nearby Red Cross building, with its quieter and more
pleasant environment. Again social factors are suggested but not conclusively incriminated.

We return for a moment to the monkeys kept in the corner of the
biochemistry laboratory, whose average excretion was about 1.5 mg

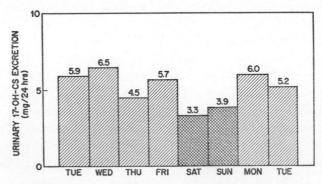

FIG. 2. Urinary 17-OH-CS excretion per 24 hr by day of week
in hospitalized human subject.

of 17-OH-CS per day. As soon as space became available so that the chair-restrained animals could be kept in a room of their own, the mean 17-OH-CS excretion rate dropped strikingly—about 50 per cent. In some instances the same animals were studied in both rooms, and it became clear that the concept of "normal" 17-OH-CS levels must be seriously re-evaluated and that perhaps the term "basal" level might be more appropriate for a system which so sensitively reflects interaction with the environment.

Most of the data presented so far seem to support the concept that the central nervous system exerts a tonicity, a continuing stimulatory influence, upon this neuroendocrine system, which reflects in a general way the quantity, and perhaps the quality, of exteroceptive input from the environment. We have come to accept that similar tonicity is exerted by the brain upon skeletal muscle and autonomic functions, and it is not surprising that we must add to these the neuroendocrine systems, which represent a third major effector output through which the brain integrates bodily functions. We shall see that this concept of pituitary–adrenal cortical activity as a general index of interaction or involvement of the animal with the physical and social environment holds up very well through subsequent more systematic experimental and clinical studies.

Corticosteroid Response to Operant Conditioning

When we initiated our more formal animal-conditioning experiments we quickly learned that the sensitivity of 17-OH-CS response to environmental factors constituted a major hindrance to reproducibility in these experiments. Corticosteroid baseline values were frequently elevated because of activity, noise, or other events that occurred in preparing for experiments or in connection with other monkeys in the same room. A primary objective in these studies almost from the beginning then became the rigorous control of extraneous physical and social stimuli, which culminated in the use of individual sound-resistant cubicles or booths for each experimental animal. The paucity of data on social processes in subsequent conditioning experiments needs no further comment, but perhaps several aspects of the experiments deserve mention because of possible future methodological significance.

First, while we have employed food-reward or shock-aversive reinforcement procedures almost exclusively, it has often occurred to us that the significance of social factors could readily be studied within our methodological framework, and that social stimuli might well extend both the variety and the intensity of emotional or psychoendocrine responses for experimental analysis in the monkey.

That monkeys can function as relevant social stimuli in such emotional conditioning situations has been amply demonstrated by the work of Miller, Murphy, and Mirsky (1955) at Pittsburgh, and by that of Hansen and Mason (1962) at Wisconsin. Not only can one monkey serve as a discriminative stimulus for the establishment and maintenance of shock-avoidance behavior in a second monkey, but the dominance status of such stimulus animals increases significantly. In addition, the facial expression and posture of such stimulus monkeys has been demonstrated to exercise differential discriminative control over the rate of avoidance responding in the conditioned "partner" monkey (Miller, Murphy, and Mirsky, 1959; Miller, Banks, and Ogawa, 1962). Indeed, our early studies with rhesus monkeys in the "yoked" chair situation shown in Fig. 3 in which

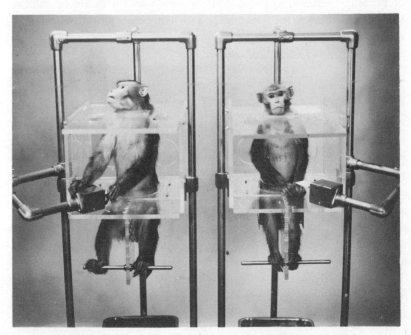

Fig. 3. Social interaction between monkey pairs in avoidance
conditioning to shock.

shock administration to pairs of monkeys was controlled by the avoidance performance of only one member of the pair, revealed some distinct social interactions between these primates. Administration of a shock following a pause of 20 seconds by the experimental animal frequently elicited from the control monkey vocal tirades that were accurately directed at the avoidance member of the pair. In fact, during later phases of this work when as many as six or eight monkeys were lined up side by side in chairs with a control monkey between two experimental animals, the control animals quickly discriminated which of the two avoidance monkeys was the appropriate object for expressions of displeasure following shock.

Although it is clear that such social interaction is not a necessary condition for the development of the gastrointestinal pathology observed in our monkeys during the avoidance performance, we are still without a completely satisfactory explanation for the consistently higher incidence of peptic ulcers in our initial series of socially interacting monkey pairs (Brady *et al.*, 1958). When in subsequent experiments all animals were individually housed within sound-resistant, light-tight booths, which prevented such social interaction, the avoidance monkeys continued to show selective pathological changes, although the extent and frequency of these effects were markedly attenuated. Of course, several other experimental manipulations were involved in these subsequent studies, including critical changes in the work–rest cycles, but it is provocative to consider the potentially important contributory role of the social influences in the initially high incidence of behaviorally induced illness. Certainly, the consistent and marked hormonal changes observed in these monkeys performing on the 6-hour "on," 6-hour "off" avoidance schedule support the suggestion that strong emotional factors, both social and non-social in origin, contribute significantly to the development of such pathological changes.

In a somewhat more systematic program, we have for some years been concerned with the specific nature of the behavioral conditioning situations that produce durable alterations in physiological processes, particularly in the activity of the pituitary–adrenal cortical system. The subjects in these experiments have been rhesus monkeys restrained in primate chairs as illustrated in Fig. 3, and behavioral performances have been generated and maintained by using both appetitive and aversive control procedures. Monkeys reinforced with food on either a continuous or a fixed ratio schedule display no elevations in plasma 17-OH-CS levels during the course of an experimental session. Nor is there any evidence of an appreciable adrenal-cortical response in the monkeys when their reinforcement schedules are abruptly shifted from low to high fixed ratios and even to extinction. Two of the behavioral procedures involved in this analysis, however, do produce marked elevations in plasma 17-OH-CS levels (Mason, Brady, and Sidman, 1957).

One of these effective procedures is a modification of the Estes-Skinner conditioned suppression technique. Monkeys pressing levers for food on a variable-interval schedule are given occasional unavoidable shocks, each shock preceded by a warning stimulus. The animals typically cease pressing the lever when the warning stimuli are presented, and all five monkeys studied using this procedure consistently showed marked increases in plasma 17-OH-CS levels during the experimental sessions. Significantly, this increased adrenal-cortical activity occurs even though shock is never administered during experimental sessions in which hormone measurements are made. Within 1 hour after the termination of such a conditioned "anxiety" session, however, plasma 17-OH-CS levels return to pre-experimental baseline values in virtually all cases. A further analysis of this relationship between conditioned suppression and corticosteroid elevation has shown that repeated doses of reserpine (0.75 mg/kg) administered 20 to 22 hours before the experimental sessions markedly attenuate the "anxiety" response and eliminate the corticosteroid elevation (Mason and Brady, 1956).

A second effective procedure used in this analysis is conditioned avoidance (Sidman, 1953). Brief electric shocks to the animal's feet are programmed every 20 seconds without an exteroceptive warning stimulus. Each time the monkey presses the lever, however, it postpones the shock for 20 seconds. Performance on such an avoidance schedule for 2 hours is invariably associated with twofold to fourfold rises in corticosteroid levels for virtually all animals, even in those experiments where the monkey successfully avoids all shocks. Although plasma 17-OH-CS levels have been observed to return to pre-experimental baseline values within a few hours after the termination of such avoidance sessions, repeated exposures with several animals during continuing weekly sessions clearly demonstrate the persistence of this pituitary-adrenal response to the avoidance situation (Mason, Brady, and Sidman, 1957).

A more detailed analysis of this relation between avoidance behavior and pituitary–adrenal cortical activity has focused upon the quantitative aspects of the relations between corticosteroid levels and some of the variables relevant to avoidance behavior in an attempt to determine which features of the avoidance procedure are involved in the corticosteroid elevations.

We have been concerned, for example, with the effects of varying the response–shock interval of the avoidance requirement in relation to changes in corticosteroid levels. The general picture suggests that the higher rates of lever pressing produced by shorter response–shock intervals are accompanied by higher 17-OH-CS levels, although it was not clear at first whether these transient elevations could be accounted for in terms of changes in the response–shock interval, in shock frequency, or in the rate of avoidance responding per se. A comparison between discriminated and nondiscriminated avoidance procedures in relation to 17-OH-CS changes, however, has made it possible to hold the response–shock interval constant while demonstrating covariance of the lever-pressing rate and the corticosteroid level. Even under these conditions, however, it is clear that shock frequency plays a very strong determining role in both the 17-OH-CS level and the lever-pressing rate increases. We have had some success, however, in disentangling the independent effects of lever-pressing rate and shock frequency upon the 17-OH-CS response. When shock frequency is kept constant while the rate of lever pressing declines in an extended avoidance-extinction procedure with accompanying brief unavoidable shocks superimposed every two minutes, no elevations in 17-OH-CS levels were observed, clearly implicating the animal's lever-pressing behavior as at least one important correlate of the corticosteroid change. Similarly, manipulation of the avoidance-response rate by a stimulus-control procedure involving a warning stimulus in a well-established discriminated avoidance performance supports this finding that the lever-pressing behavior per se can activate the pituitary–adrenal cortical system independently of the shocks. In these experiments, frequent presentation of the warning stimulus generated a relatively high response rate without changing the shock frequency, and a substantial 17-OH-CS elevation was elicited even though not a single shock was received during the 2-hour experimental sessions (Sidman *et al.*, 1962).

Catechol Amine Response to Operant Conditioning

The conditioning studies up to this point strongly support the conclusion that 17-OH-CS measurements provide a reliable and useful indicator, making possible a quantitative estimate of the intensity and duration of psychoendocrine, and presumably emotional, responses to specific stimuli. Again the evidence supports a relatively non-specific, undifferentiated character of the correlated behavioral change, perhaps suggesting more a category like distress, arousal, or involvement, than specific responses like fear or anger. It was only as the study of additional endocrine systems and more elaborate hormone patterns became possible that the promise of the psychoendocrine approach in differentiating emotional responses was realized. Concurrent biochemical measurements of plasma 17-OH-CS, norepinephrine, and epinephrine levels during a performance on several different operant-conditioning procedures have provided the focus for some of our recent efforts in this direction. Under conditions similar to those described above, both the Estes-Skinner conditioned-suppression technique and Sidman avoidance during sessions of only 30 minutes' duration were observed to produce consistent elevations in both 17-OH-CS and norepinephrine levels, with little or no change in plasma epinephrine. Marked epinephrine elevations were apparent, however, in studies that measured hormone changes in monkeys during relatively brief 10-minute intervals preceding the start of an experimental session in which the performance requirements were varied and unpredictable. The animals in these latter experiments had been trained on a series of multiple-schedule procedures with conditioned suppression, Sidman avoidance, discriminated punishment, variable-interval food reinforcement alone, and S^Δ or "time out" components, all under the control of different stimulus conditions (colored lights, clicks, etc.). Sessions on such multiple schedules were initiated by different components presented in random order on different days, and dramatic alterations in the hormone pattern were observed during the 10-minute interval immediately preceding these sessions. The withdrawal of blood from the monkey's vein served as a warning signal that the performance sessions would begin 10 minutes afterward. Significantly, such epinephrine elevations could not be observed when the experimental session began immediately after the withdrawal of the blood sample, regardless of which multiple-schedule component initiated the performance. Even in those experiments that involved large epinephrine elevations during the 10-minute pre-session waiting period, blood samples taken within 1½ minutes after the presentation of the stimulus signaling the first multiple-schedule component revealed precipitous drops in the epinephrine levels, which consistently remained low throughout the rest of the session (Mason, Mangan, et al., 1961).

Patterns of Endocrine Response

Patterns of corticosteroid and pepsinogen levels in rhesus monkeys have been analyzed in relation to performance on the Sidman avoidance procedure during continuous 72-hour-long experimental sessions (Mason, Brady, Polish, et al., 1961). Although the plasma 17-OH-CS levels showed the expected substantial elevation throughout the 72-hour avoidance session, plasma pepsinogen levels were consistently depressed below baseline values during this same period. Significantly, however, the post-avoidance recovery for all of the animals in this study was characterized by a marked and prolonged elevation of pepsinogen levels, which endured for several days beyond the 48-hour post-avoidance interval required for recovery of the pre-avoidance corticosteroid baseline.

Most recently, this "endocrine pattern" approach has been extended to include a broader spectrum of hormonal changes in relation to emotional disturbances in the rhesus monkey (Mason, Brady, Tolson, et al., 1961). Alterations in thyroid, gonadal, and adrenal hormone secretion patterns were produced by a continuous 72-hour experimental session on Sidman avoidance, and the endocrinological consequences of exposure to this behavioral stress were detectable for prolonged periods following its termination. The 17-OH-CS and epinephrine levels were at least twice the baseline value during the avoidance session but returned to normal within 2 to 6 days. Androsterone and estrone levels dropped to below half the baseline value during avoidance but showed substantial rebound changes above baseline from 3 to 6 days after the completion of the session. There was little change in the thyroid levels during the initial portions of the avoidance performance period, but a gradual elevation throughout the session produced a peak value early in the post-avoidance recovery period, which in some instances did not return to baseline for a full 3 weeks after the end of the 3-day session.

Neurological Mechanisms

The operant avoidance technique, reliably producing alterations in hormone levels, has also been used to advantage in studies involving neurological mechanisms controlling endocrine balance. Mason, Nauta, *et al.* (1961), have reported that the increase in 17-OH-CS levels which invariably accompanies Sidman avoidance performance during 2-hour-long sessions is substantially diminished in monkeys following bilateral removal of the amygdala nuclei. Although this suppressing effect of amygdalectomy on the corticosteroid response to avoidance develops only 4 to 6 weeks post-operatively, as long as one year after surgery, elevations in the hormone levels cannot be observed during performance on the standard Sidman schedule. When a "free shock" procedure is superimposed upon the avoidance baseline, however, a marked elevation of the 17-OH-CS level does appear, indicating that the system is capable of responding under somewhat extreme conditions even in the absence of the presumed modulation or facilitation normally provided by the amygdaloid complex (Mason, Nauta, *et al.*, 1961).

Clearly, the application of behavioral conditioning methodology in these carefully controlled psychophysiological studies continues to provide a powerful tool for the experimental analysis of conditions that differentially alter endocrine response patterns. The analysis of social factors by modification of this methodology remains largely a promising prospect for the future.

Clinical Studies

We should like to turn finally to some incidental observations in clinical studies that have suggested social influences on psychoendocrine systems. As reported previously, we have observed a tendency in some small groups of 5 to 6 individuals for 17-OH-CS levels to cluster in a rather narrow range, basally and during stress, after the group has lived or worked together for a while (Mason, 1959). One of the first observations to suggest this notion was in a small crew of a B-52 jet bomber on a non-stop round trip flight to Argentina. While the instructor pilot, with the major responsibilities of piloting and supervising hazardous mid-air refueling of the aircraft, had extremely high levels of 20 mg/day (compared with a mean normal of about 7 mg/day in men), the other three crewmen, who were back in the plane working closely together, all ran similar elevated levels of about 13 mg/day (Mason, 1959). Having seen relatively few values as high as 13 mg/day in hundreds of human urine samples, we were struck with the possibility that a socially communicated "13-mg/day" atmosphere may have prevailed in this craft on the flight day. On non-flight days, levels in these subjects were quite different and substantially lower.

We have observed phenomena that are perhaps similar in studies of hospitalized normal young adults conducted in collaboration with Dr. David Hamburg and members of the Adult Psychiatry Branch at the National Institute of Mental Health (NIMH). Groups of 7 to 13 college-age adults were admitted to a "normal control" volunteer ward and lived closely together for weeks or months while a variety of psychological and endocrine observations were made. Table 3 shows the urinary 17-OH-CS levels on the first day of hospital admission and on a later date after the group had lived together for a week or longer. In the first two groups there appears to be a tendency for individual levels to cluster quite closely after a period of hospitalization, though with somewhat different mean values for each group. The third group, however, does not show this tendency, and levels remained scattered as shown after 5 weeks on the ward. Systematic observations of social factors were not available in these groups, but some gross cultural and social distinctions can be suggested. The fact that the third group included both sexes, while the other two groups were composed entirely of girls, appears to be one possibly relevant factor. It has been reported in the total study of a larger number of subjects that girls in mixed groups had significantly higher mean 17-OH-CS values than girls in all-girl groups (Fishman *et al.*, 1962). In any event these data suggest the need for systematic evaluation of social factors and create an interest in the group dynamics of the ward population.

Similar data that show a tendency for clustering of plasma 17-OH-CS levels in small groups of soldiers anticipating sleep-deprivation

TABLE 3

*Urinary 17-OH-CS Levels in Different Groups of
Hospitalized Normal Young Adults*

Urine 17-OH-CS levels (mg/24 hr)	Group 1 Day 1	Group 1 Day 35	Group 2 Day 1	Group 2 Day 8–11	Group 3 Day 1	Group 3 Day 35
20						
19						
18						
17					X	
16						
15						
14			X		X	
13						
12						X
11	X		X		X	
10			X		X	X
9			X			X
8			XX			
7	X		XX	XX	X	XX
6	XX		XXX	XX		X
5	XXXX	XXXX	XX	XXXX	X	
4	X	XXXX		XX	X	X
3	XXX	XXXX		XX		
2	X					
1						
0						

experiments have been reported (Mason, 1959). We might add to this some recent observations in young adults on the "normal control" NIMH ward, who were serving as subjects in studies of psychoendocrine responses to movies. As Fig. 4 indicates, we again see a tendency for most members of the group to reach an equilibrium level, or at least to have similar absolute 17-OH-CS levels, in the basal samples withdrawn for control values prior to a movie-viewing experiment. Again observations of social processes were not included in the experimental design, which was concerned primarily with mood changes associated with the film-viewing experience (Handlon *et al.*, 1962; Wadeson *et al.*, 1963). One other observation of possible interest might be mentioned. The design of the movie experiments involved the withdrawal of two blood samples prior to the film viewing, the first about 1½ to 3 hours before, and the second immediately before the movie. In the first experiment of this kind, subjects were given

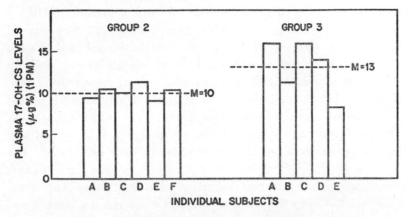

FIG. 4. Plasma 17-OH-CS levels in two groups before movie experiments.

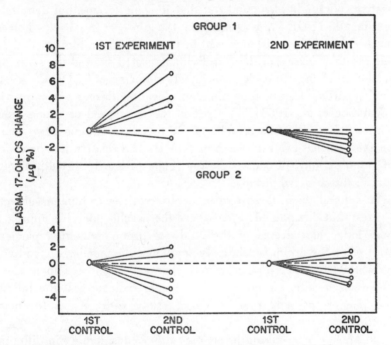

FIG. 5. Effect of pre-experimental ambiguity on the human 17-OH-CS response.

minimal information about the film experiment; they were told only that we would like to study their hormonal responses to viewing a film, and the rest was essentially left to their imaginations. Figure 5 shows that in this rather ambiguous waiting period, during which the members of the group conversed and speculated about the forthcoming experience, 4 of 5 subjects showed a plasma 17-OH-CS elevation (Wadeson *et al.*, 1963). Shortly afterward they learned that ordinary commercial movies were to be shown, and a week later on their second experience no such elevations occurred. In order to minimize this effect in the next group, since it interfered with the interpretation of hormonal changes during the movie period itself, subjects were subsequently given fuller information about the experiment and the kind of film to be shown. It is evident that the next group does not show this effect in their experiment. The extent to which the first group might have shown the same changes even if individuals had been rigorously isolated, rather than in social contact, during the pre-film period is of course, not known, and again the evidence for the operation of social influences is only suggestive. We might also point out that in some groups, but definitely not in all, 17-OH-CS responses to the film-viewing itself showed marked internal consistency within the group from film to film. In one group at least 5 of the 6 individuals tested showed the same direction of change in each experiment, a decline of 17-OH-CS levels during Disney nature films and an elevation during a war movie (Wadeson *et al.*, 1963). This group was composed of young men, conscientious objectors, who had lived together for almost two years on the "normal control" ward at NIMH. The relative homogeneity of response may, of course, simply relate primarily to cultural factors in this selected group.

In general, then, these scattered observations in human subjects suggest that one possible area where the psychoendocrine approach may have relevance is in the study of group dynamics, particularly when the group is relatively small and the members have lived or worked together in a relatively intimate setting for some time. More specifically, hormone measurements indicate that the following phenomena may deserve closer study with respect to social factors:

1. Mean corticosteroid levels may differ considerably in different small groups brought into similar settings.

2. Some small groups have a very narrow range of intragroup corticosteroid values, with perhaps just 1 deviant subject out of 5 or 6, while other groups show a wide range of intragroup individual variation in a similar setting and under similar conditions.

Another possible approach that we have not explored at all might be the experimental manipulation of interpersonal relationships within the group as a means of systematically inducing emotional changes in particular subjects. Laboratory attempts to induce emotional, or at least psychoendocrine, changes in the human by contrived means have generally been unsuccessful, and the group setting might, by its more naturalistic character, offer advantages over the laboratory investigator–subject settings.

It would be quite misleading, however, to conclude by leaving the impression that most people show rather labile pituitary–adrenal cortical activity which can quickly equilibrate at different absolute levels when conditions change. Actually the phenomena just described probably occur only under rather special conditions which have been only partially defined as yet, and it is much more common in our prolonged situational stress studies with humans to see clearly defined individual differences in mean corticosteroid excretion sustained over long periods of time. Subjects such as the parents of leukemic children can be characterized as chronic "highs," "middles," or "lows" with respect to mean 17-OH-CS excretion, and often show remarkably little fluctuation within their own narrow range (Friedman, Mason, and Hamburg, 1963). When changes in levels do occur, they almost always seem better correlated with situational factors involving the child's illness, or with personality factors, rather than with social influences. In fact, current psychiatric studies with these subjects indicate that mean 17-OH-CS levels can be predicted with a high degree of reliability on the basis of the evaluation of personality characteristics relating to psychological defenses, to tension-relieving activities, or more broadly, to a range of behavioral mechanisms habitually employed in dealing with distressing events or thoughts (Wolff *et al.*, 1964a, 1964b). Occasionally, when one of these mechanisms, such as denial, is temporarily undermined or ineffective, as for example in the mother of a fatally ill child, dramatic changes may occur in the prevailing level of corticosteroid excretion.

Conclusions

It appears then that the psychoendocrine approach may afford access to the study not only of emotionality in the sense of quantitating or differentiating affective changes, but also of the very broad range

of normal and abnormal psychological functions which serve to prevent, minimize, or counteract affective disturbances. The recent studies of Friedman, Mason, and Hamburg (1963), Sachar *et al.*
(1963), and Wolff *et al.* (1963) show that impressive evidence is
accumulating in support of this notion, and it seems likely that this
may eventually prove to be a major area of applicability of the psychoendocrine approach in psychiatry. To the extent that emotional
and defensive mechanisms are of interest in studies of social processes,
it seems then that this approach may be useful to investigators in the
field of social behavior.

REFERENCES

Brady, J. V., Porter, R. W., Conrad, D. G., and Mason, J. W. Avoidance be-
havior and the development of gastroduodenal ulcers. *J. exp. Anal. Behav.*,
1958, 1, 69–72.
Christian, J. J. Phenomena associated with population density. *Proc. Nat.
Acad. Sci., Wash.*, 1961, 47, 428–49.
Fishman, J. R., Hamburg, D. A., Handlon, J. H., Mason, J. W., and Sachar,
E. J. Emotional and adrenal cortical responses to a new experience. *A.M.A.
Arch. gen. Psychiat.*, 1962, 6, 271–78.
Friedman, S. B., Mason, J. W., and Hamburg, D. A. Urinary 17-hydroxycorti-
costeroid levels in parents of children with neoplastic disease. *Psychosom.
Med.*, 1963, 25, 364–76.
Handlon, J. H., Wadeson, R. W., Fishman, J. R., Sachar, E. J., Hamburg,
D. A., and Mason, J. W. Psychological factors lowering plasma 17-hydroxy-
corticosteroid concentration. *Psychosom. Med.*, 1962, 24, 535–42.
Hansen, E. W., and Mason, W. A. Socially mediated changes in lever-respond-
ing of rhesus monkeys. *Psychol. Rep.*, 1962, 11, 647–54.
Mason, J. W. Psychological influences on the pituitary–adrenal cortical sys-
tem. *Recent Progress in Hormone Research*, 1959, 15, 345–89.
Mason, J. W., and Brady, J. V. Plasma 17-hydroxycorticosteroid changes re-
lated to reserpine effects on emotional behavior. *Science*, 1956, 124, 983–84.
Mason, J. W., Brady, J. V., and Sidman, M. Plasma 17-hydroxycorticosteroid
levels and conditioned behavior in the rhesus monkey. *Endocrinology*, 1957,
60, 741–52.
Mason, J. W., Brady, J. V., Polish, E., Bauer, J. A., Robinson, J. A., Rose,
R. M., and Taylor, E. D. Patterns of corticosteroid and pepsinogen change
related to emotional stress in the monkey. *Science*, 1961, 133, 1596–98.
Mason, J. W., Brady, J. V., Tolson, W. W., Robinson, J. A., Taylor, E. D., and
Mougey, E. H. Patterns of thyroid, gonadal, and adrenal hormone excre-

tion related to psychological stress in the monkey. *Psychosom. Med.*, 1961, 23, 446 (Abstract).

Mason, J. W., Mangan, G. F., Jr., Brady, J. V., Conrad, D., and Rioch, D. McK. Concurrent plasma epinephrine, norepinephrine and 17-hydroxycorticosteroid levels during conditioned emotional disturbances in monkeys. *Psychosom. Med.*, 1961, 23, 344–53.

Mason, J. W., Nauta, W. J. H., Brady, J. V., Robinson, J. A., and Sachar, E. J. The role of limbic system structures in the regulation of ACTH secretion. *Acta Neurovegetativa*, 1961, 23, 4–14.

Miller, R. E., Murphy, J. V., and Mirsky, I. A. The modification of social dominance in a group of monkeys by interanimal conditioning. *J. comp. physiol. Psychol.*, 1955, 48, 392–96.

Miller, R. E., Murphy, J. V., and Mirsky, I. A. Relevance of facial expression and posture as cues in communication of affect between monkeys. *A.M.A. Arch. gen. Psychiat.*, 1959, 1, 480–88.

Miller, R. E., Banks, J. H., and Ogawa, N. Communication of affect in "cooperative conditioning" of rhesus monkeys. *J. abnorm. soc. Psychol.*, 1962, 64, 343–48.

Sachar, E. J., Mason, J. W., Kolmer, H. S., and Artiss, K. L. Psychoendocrine aspects of acute schizophrenic reactions. *Psychosom. Med.*, 1963, 25, 510–37.

Sidman, M. Avoidance conditioning with brief shock and no exteroceptive warning signal. *Science*, 1953, 118, 157–58.

Sidman, M., Mason, J. W., Brady, J. V., and Thach, J. S., Jr. Quantitative relations between avoidance behavior and pituitary–cortical activity in rhesus monkeys. *J. exp. Anal. Behav.*, 1962, 5, 353–62.

Thiessen, D. D., and Rodgers, D. A. Population density and endocrine function. *Psychol. Bull.*, 1961, 58, 441–51.

Wadeson, R., Mason, J. W., Hamburg, D. A., and Handlon, J. H. Plasma and urinary 17-OH-CS rseponses to motion pictures. *A.M.A. Arch. gen. Psychiat.*, 1963, 9, 146–56.

Wolff, C. T., Friedman, S. B., Hofer, M. A., and Mason, J. W. Relationship between psychological defenses and mean urinary 17-OH-CS excretion rates: I. A predictive study of parents of fatally ill children. *Psychosom. Med.*, 1964a, 26, 576–91.

Wolff, C. T., Hofer, M. A., and Mason, J. W. Relationship between psychological defenses and mean urinary 17-OH-CS excretion rates: II. Methodological and theoretical considerations. *Psychosom. Med.*, 1964b, 26, 592–609.

Plasma Lipid Responses to Leadership, Conformity, and Deviation

KURT W. BACK AND MORTON D. BOGDONOFF
Duke University

In an attempt to assess the physiological consequences of behavioral events in man, investigators have measured many different variables. Most often, investigations have focused on those functions which are most directly related to activity of the autonomic nervous system, such as galvanic skin resistance, heart rate, blood pressure, and plasma glucose concentration. In addition, whenever the experimental design permitted, urinary excretion of catechol amines has been measured, in order to obtain a more direct index of adrenal medulla and sympathetic nerve activity.

In our laboratory we have recently observed that the level of a lipid component of the plasma—the free fatty acid (FFA)—is rapidly and significantly modified by events which might be expected to alter autonomic nervous system activity. In the studies reported in this chapter, serial measurements of plasma FFA level have been used as a dependent variable, and the nature of social interaction between individuals has been the experimentally controlled independent variable.

The FFA component of the plasma consists of sodium salts of long-chain carbon compounds (C-10-20), which are presumably derived from the fatty acids that constitute the triglycerides of adipose tissue.

These investigations were supported by the Office of Naval Research, Group Psychology Branch (Contract No. 1181 11, Project NR 177 470), the Life Insurance Medical Research Fund, the National Institutes of Health (M-5356), the Duke University Center for the Study of Aging, and the Irwin Strasburger Memorial Fund. The authors wish to acknowledge the participation and help in the experiments of Mary L. Brehm, Thomas C. Hood, and Barbara Hyatt, and technical help in chemical analysis by Gitta Jackson.

In adipose tissue there are lipolytic enzymes, which have the property of cleaving the fatty acids from the glycerol of the triglyceride molecule. This process of lipolysis may be stimulated by a number of compounds. Both *in vitro* and *in vivo* studies have indicated that the release of free fatty acids from adipose tissue triglyceride is stimulated by growth hormone, adrenocorticotropic hormone (ACTH), thyroid extract, corticosteroids, epinephrine, and norepinephrine. Once the fatty acids are cleaved from the triglyceride of adipose tissue, the FFA may enter the extracellular fluid space, appear next in the plasma, and then be transported to various tissues. It is believed that FFA may provide the prime source of substrate for energy-demanding processes in the skeletal muscle, and in that manner the lipid of the adipose tissue may be said to have been mobilized to the working muscle.

A series of studies of changes in plasma FFA level during various procedures and hormone infusions has indicated that in the fasting, non-exercising individual, the moment-to-moment change in plasma FFA level may serve as an approximate index of autonomic activity. Figure 1 summarizes these studies and indicates how various degrees of increase in plasma FFA level may be interpreted as reflecting various degrees of autonomic activity initiated by the intensity of central nervous system arousal (Bogdonoff *et al.*, 1961a).

Medical Background

In recent years a special interest in plasma lipids has developed as a relationship between lipid metabolism and coronary artery atherosclerosis has become more likely. Although the cause of this disease is unknown, epidemiological surveys have suggested that the eating habits and the patterns of behavior of certain social groups may be related to alterations in plasma lipid levels and to the development of this disorder. Keys has reported that individuals eating a diet high in saturated fat (such as the well-to-do Neapolitans) have a high rate of coronary atherosclerosis (Keys *et al.*, 1954). Morris has reported that the incidence of this disease is higher among the men who drive the busses of London than it is among the men who collect fares on the same busses. He suggested that the differences in physical activity and "stress" might be important (Morris, 1959). Because daily life in modern-day Western society appears to generate an impressive de-

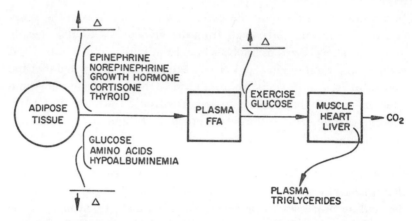

Fig. 1. Schematic diagram illustrating the factors that modify the concentration of plasma free fatty acid (FFA). The diagram attempts to indicate that the plasma FFA derives from adipose tissue. Those factors that promote mobilization ($\uparrow\Delta$) are grouped above the line; those that decrease mobilization ($\downarrow\Delta$) are listed below the line. The factors on the right indicate those changes that promote FFA utilization in the peripheral tissues. Central nervous system stimuli are believed to operate through the epinephrine and norepinephrine pathway.

gree of "stress," the relationship of the behavioral and psychological characteristics of the individual to the natural history of these diseases has also been studied. Friedman and Rosenman (1959) studied accountants before and during the time of particular urgency in their work patterns (income tax report deadline) and concluded that individuals who persistently demonstrated an "overt behavior pattern characterized by excessive and competitive drive and an enhanced sense of time urgency exhibited . . . an approximately sevenfold higher incidence of clinical coronary artery disease." Wolf (1958) reported development of acute myocardial infarction during specific life-situational difficulties.

One of the important pathological features of coronary artery atherosclerosis is the presence of lipid deposits (cholesterol-containing plaques) in the walls of the coronary arteries, and many studies have been conducted in which a relationship between the concentration of cholesterol in the blood and the incidence of coronary artery atherosclerosis has been demonstrated (Gofman *et al.*, 1952; Kannel *et al.*, 1961). Both Friedman and Rosenman, and Wolf, in their studies of stress and behavior as related to coronary artery disease, observed that the plasma cholesterol levels increased significantly before and during the clinical event of coronary artery occlusion. Thus, a link between patterns of behavior, alterations in plasma cholesterol level, and coronary artery disease has been suggested.

The clinical observations on the changes of plasma cholesterol levels with stress have been extended to experimental studies in the laboratory, and during circumscribed periods of stimulated arousal, cholesterol levels do increase significantly (Thomas and Murphy, 1958; Wertlake et al., 1958). In addition, plasma FFA level was observed to increase markedly during periods characterized by central nervous system arousal. The rapid rises in plasma FFA levels were interpreted as representing increased degrees of fat mobilization, and a number of studies have been conducted in which a relation between the process of fat mobilization and behavioral responses has been shown.

Initially, it was observed that the discussion of psychologically meaningful past experiences resulted in acute increases in plasma FFA concentration. These discussions were accompanied by facial color and expression changes and by verbal statements by the subjects that they experienced feelings of fear, anxiety, and anger during the studies. The magnitude of the increases in plasma FFA level far exceeded the changes that might have occurred if no such focused discussions had been conducted (Bogdonoff, Estes, and Trout, 1959). Over a five-year period we have obtained a series of observations on metabolically normal individuals who were observed in the fasting, nonexercising state. We have been able to gauge the rise in FFA level that will occur when the subject is fasted and at rest (Bogdonoff et al., 1961b). The conditions of fasting and nonexercising are important in assessing the contribution of central nervous system activity to FFA levels, since carbohydrate (Dole, 1956) and exercise (Friedberg et al., 1960) will, of themselves, affect plasma FFA levels.

In a second series of studies conducted before, during, and after a stressful scholastic examination, increases in plasma FFA level were related to simultaneous measures of heart rate, electrocardiographic pattern, arterial blood pressure, plasma glucose, and rate of urinary excretion of adrenalin and noradrenalin (Bogdonoff et al., 1960a). The correlation between cardiovascular and metabolic changes with the neurohumoral alterations was consistent with other observations relating central nervous system activity to lipid metabolism (Bogdonoff, 1960). The occurrence of these changes was also supported by observations of the effect of the catechol amines upon lipid mobilization (Bogdonoff *et al.*, 1961b) and of the effect of the autonomic nervous system on plasma FFA levels (Bogdonoff *et al.*, 1960b).

Plasma FFA is useful in experiments in social psychology for the following reasons:

1. Plasma FFA is a very sensitive indicator of autonomic nervous system activation.

2. Plasma FFA changes accurately reflect the process of lipid mobilization; the process of lipid mobilization may play a role in the evolution of lipid deposits in vessel walls, and hence in the occurrence of atherosclerosis. Experimental analogs to life stresses can, therefore, be analyzed in their effects on FFA and compared with the epidemiological studies of life stresses.

3. Plasma FFA changes are sufficiently rapid to be measured within the framework of an experiment, although they are not rapid enough to provide a continuous record.

4. The measurement process is stressful in itself, since blood samples have to be obtained from the subject. This circumstance, in turn, leads to heightened awareness of the experimental situation and makes the FFA measures dependent, in part, on the subject's reaction to the experimental situation per se (Brehm, Back, and Bogdonoff, 1964).

5. Serial measurements of plasma FFA during laboratory experiments in group interaction provide an independent index of arousal (and presumably of the meaning of the situation at the time) without the attendant difficulties of questionnaire measures, e.g., possible conscious distortion and contamination.

The experimental variables of primary importance in our studies of FFA are those which have shown themselves to be of significance in the epidemiological studies, namely, stress from situational demands and group interactions. The experimental situation that seemed most appropriate to initial social psychological work with FFA was the standard conformity experiment which allowed variations in task characteristics and relation to and interaction with other group members (Back, 1951). The procedure is described in detail below. Since the FFA level is sensitive to autonomic arousal from whatever source, the subject's reaction to the experimental situation, and his relation to the other group members, as well as the specifically introduced independent variables, all may prove to be important. The four experiments to be described below will show the different ways in which we arrived at a measure of the physiological arousal for relationships between the members of the experimental group.

General Experimental Procedure

The model for the experimental procedure was designed as follows. Young male subjects (undergraduate students, without known metabolic disease) were fasted for 10 to 12 hours and directed to report to the laboratory in groups of four. On arrival they were received by one of the experimenters. An indwelling Cournand needle was placed into a forearm (antecubital) vein, and sample number 1 was drawn. All samples were collected in heparinized syringes, immediately cooled, and then centrifuged in a Lourdes refrigerated centrifuge. Samples were analyzed for FFA by a modification of the method used by Dole (1956). For the next 30 minutes the subjects sat quietly in the laboratory filling out a personal history and psychological questionnaire. Sample number 2 was then drawn. The 30-minute interval between the first two samples was purposely provided, since our previous observations had shown that the process of needle puncture may alter the resting level of plasma FFA. The next phase of the run included the task instruction. These instructions were memorized by the experimenter and presented to each group of subjects in as similar a manner as possible.

The task itself consisted in matching one of three stimuli with a standard stimulus. The stimulus was a projected image. The subjects were instructed to answer the question by pressing one of three keys on a panel on an apparatus similar to those designed by Crutchfield (1955) and Gerard (1961).

Ostensibly the subjects answered in turn and each subject saw the answer of the others by the lights on his panel. Actually, in conformity conditions each subject was the last in turn (Subject D), and the answers that represented the other subjects (Subjects A, B, and C) were programmed by hidden switches. In leadership conditions the subject went first (Subject A), and the subsequent responses (B, C, and D) were programmed. In this way conflicts could be created at will. Subjects could give their response before or after the lights which ostensibly represented the other subjects were turned on. Thus different conditions of agreement and disagreement could be created. The instructions also included special explanations according to experimental conditions. Subjects then did a few practice trials in which the other subjects' lights were not turned on. Blood sample number 3 was drawn after the instructions had been given. Subsequent samples were drawn at test intervals determined by the specific design of each study.

The series of FFA measurements makes it possible to assess physiologic responses to two different situations: those related to the entry into the experimental situation as such, and those connected with the experimentally introduced variables. For the former, the reaction to the experiment, the plasma FFA level at the time of the second blood sample (resting level) may serve as a measure of arousal within the experimental situation; another measure, representing the stress and anxiety of the start of the experiment and the puncture of the needle, is the relation of the FFA level of the initial sample (right after the puncture) to the FFA level of the second sample. For the effects of the experimental variables themselves, the measures at the last period of the experiment (or sometimes the next to the last) and the changes during these periods are relevant.

In this chapter we shall deal with the experimental variables of conformity and leadership, and shall therefore concentrate on the differences between the last-period measures of the experimental conditions. In this way discussion of the initial conditions will be omitted, but we shall attempt at times to control these initial differences. The standardization measures used gave us confidence that the results were the function of the experimental variables, although in conjunction with some—here unspecified personality traits—which are represented in the initial FFA levels.

Cohesion and Ability

In the first study, experimentally created cohesiveness and experimentally induced ability were the independent variables. Both were induced by previously used techniques. Three kinds of cohesion were created by the instructions: high cohesion by announcing that the groups were especially well matched, no cohesion where matching was not stressed, and negative cohesion by announcing that the groups were especially poorly matched (Back, 1951). Through feedback of initial scores to each subject, the impression was created for that subject that he had performed better than the rest of the group, worse than the rest of the group, or the same as the rest of the group (Gerard, 1961). This three-by-three design created nine conditions, and four subjects were run in each condition. The most striking result of the study was the rapid increase in plasma FFA level during the instruction and manipulation period. That is, the subjects were affected as much by the definition of the situation by the experimenter, the nature of the task, and the preliminaries, as by the task and the experimental procedure itself. This remained true in all experiments (see Tables 1 and 3). This increase in plasma FFA level, however, was different in the different experimental conditions. There was also a definite pattern of conditions that related the increase during the instruction period, the change during the experimental period, and conformity. Operationally, conformity must be defined as preference for the social stimulus over the physical stimulus. What we call true conformity is rejection of the resistance to the physical stimulus because of attraction to the group. In general, those conditions in which there was the greatest increase in FFA level during the instruction period showed the greatest decrease during the experimental period, and were accompanied by the greatest degrees of conformity (see Fig. 2). The conditions in which there was a large initial increase followed by a decrease during the experiment, attended by conformity, and the conditions in which the reverse occurred, showed an interaction between cohesion and relative ability. The highest increase during the instructions occurred under conditions either of high cohesiveness and high ability or of negative cohesiveness and low ability. This could be explained by assuming that if the person is in a group to which he feels attracted, and is thrust into a position of leadership, he will feel "stress"; or, alternatively, he will feel stress if he is put into a group from which he feels somewhat rejected and which consists of people who outperform him. In the subsequent period, when he has the opportunity to conform, he does so, and this conforming behavior may provide a mechanism to reduce the stress,

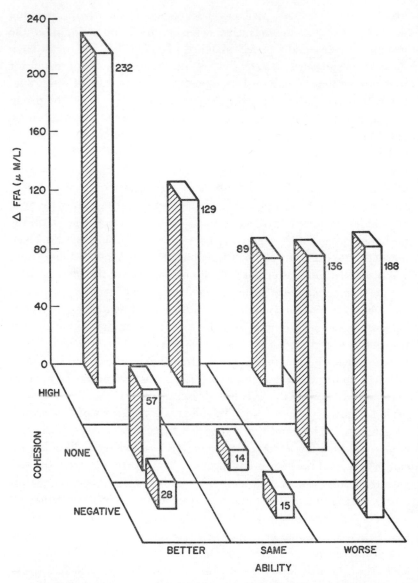

FIG. 2. Cohesion and ability. Change in FFA from resting level during instructions and trial exercises.

Variable	d.f.	F	p
Cohesion	2	2.40	<.05
Ability	2	2.24	n.s.
Interaction	4	2.63	>.05

since the elevated levels of plasma FFA tend to decrease when the subjects do conform (Back *et al.*, 1963; Bogdonoff *et al.*, 1962).

From this interpretation we concluded that conformity can mean two different things under these conditions. Conforming behavior may mean willingness to be the same as the fellow members whom one likes; this could be called *true conformity*. Conforming behavior may also be an attempt to be as good as people with whom one competes. This is actually using the judgment of others to better one's own performance, and can be called *cheating*. Conformity behavior and the accompanying stress, therefore, may really represent two completely different processes, and both processes find their analogs in the clinical studies. Thus, the high incidence of heart disease in some groups may be a function of the great efforts of the individual to succeed (Friedman and Rosenman, 1959), or it may be a function of the attempt to conform to a group norm (Morris, 1959).

Importance and Ease of Task

The next study tried to distinguish between these two kinds of conformity. Two variables were manipulated: the importance of the task and the ease of the task. It was hypothesized that the importance of the task—as created by the instructions—would produce high individual motivation to excel, and might lead to copying behavior, especially if the task was particularly difficult. If, on the other hand, the performance of the task was not considered to be important, the only reasonable basis for conformity would be the individual's desire to appear like the rest of the members of the group. This interpretation would be even more likely if the task was not only unimportant, but extremely easy to perform as well. The 48 subjects were recruited individually from a Naval ROTC squadron, and the task presented was aircraft identification. In the "important" conditions they were told that the task was very relevant to their naval training, that it was important to recognize airplanes quickly, and that their scores would be transmitted to their squadron commander. In the unimportant condition, the task was presented simply as an experiment in subliminal perception. Difficulty was manipulated by length of slide exposure: one-fifth of a second or two seconds.

The results, based on data from up to 42 of the subjects, showed different effects for importance and for difficulty. Although in a post-task questionnaire there was no significant difference between groups on rated importance of the task, there was a significantly greater rise throughout the experimental proceedings in the "important" conditions than in the "unimportant" conditions.

TABLE 1

Effect of Importance and Ease on Group Mean FFA Level

Condition	FFA level (μEq/L)				
	Sample 1	Sample 2	Sample 3	Sample 4	Sample 5
Important, difficult	949	698	777	869	987
Important, easy	814	723	673	876	932
Unimportant, difficult	604	527	619	611	613
Unimportant, easy	716	584	621	667	710

Blood samples in sequence.

As Table 1 shows, the differences between conditions occur as early as the first two blood samples, and these differences are indeed statistically significant. None of the psychological tests administered to the subjects could explain the differences adequately. Consequently, the changes in FFA level during the performance of the experimental task were divided by the resting level to obtain a standardized measure. Table 2 shows that even with this control, the "important" conditions produced a greater proportional increase.

Additional evidence of the meaning of the importance instruction was the difference in correct answers in the initial trial period, where for ten trials no feedback was given. In the "important" conditions the subjects were superior by one whole correct answer, both with easy and with difficult problems. The subjects who were told that the task was important could, therefore, be considered to be under stress. Conformity depended, however, exclusively on the difficulty of the task; subjects conformed more if they were not sure of the correct answer. There was a slight interaction between importance and difficulty in the sense that with the difficult task there was higher conformity in the important group, and with the easy task there was higher conformity in the unimportant group. This interaction was not statistically significant.

However, the same non-significant interaction occurs in the FFA change during the experimental period (in the important condition

TABLE 2

Effect of Importance and Ease on Per Cent Mean Change during Experimental Tasks

	$\dfrac{\text{Sample 5 FFA} - \text{Sample 3 FFA}}{\text{Resting level FFA}} \times 100$
Important, 1/5 sec	29
Important, 2 sec	40
Unimportant, 1/5 sec	−4
Unimportant, 2 sec	14

Analysis of Variance

Variable	Sum of squares	d.f.	M.S.	F	p
Importance	1.001	1	1.001	7.09	<.05
Time	.245	1	.245	1.74	
Interaction	.001	1	.001	.07	
Error	5.934	42	.141		

there is more change with the difficult task; in the unimportant there is more change with the easy task). Together this evidence confirms the impression that we have two principal conditions for conformity to occur: improvement of performance, as in the important, difficult condition, and adherence to group norms, as in the unimportant, easy condition.

In looking further at these two groups, we could identify two peculiar relationships to conformity in these conditions. In the important, difficult condition, conformity relates significantly to performance in the non-feedback condition ($r = .60, p < .05$), while there were non-significant negative correlations in the other three groups. As has been noted before, this performance may indicate motivation. It seems reasonable that in the condition in which conformity meant improvement of performance, this measure of conformity and performance are related. In the unimportant, easy condition, conformity did relate to decrease in FFA level ($r = .66, p < .05$). In no other condition was the relationship significant. In the two difficult conditions the conformity was related to increase in FFA level; in the important, easy condition, it was related to decrease. In the easy condition a meaningful conflict could be set up between physical stimulus and group response and, in this situation, when the individual went along with the decision of the group, this response was accompanied by a decrease in arousal. This was not true in the difficult condition, where the subject was uncertain about the improvement of his performance.

We have interpreted these results to indicate that when the task was considered to be important, the physiological arousal was so great that it was not significantly modified by conformity behavior. However, in the unimportant condition, where the baseline level of arousal was much lower, the type of behavior that an individual demonstrated did modify the intensity of the physiological response. In the unimportant, easy task condition, conforming behavior is most likely an example of true conformity, whereby the individual's adherence to the standard of the group results in a reduction of arousal. In the important, difficult condition, conforming behavior is most likely a form of copying or cheating, and despite the employment of such a behavioral response, the neurohumoral arousal is not modified.

One of the implications of the second experiment was that the group condition was not of itself a sufficiently well established variable. It was possible to create attraction among the experimental subjects, as in the first experiment, but the experimental condition overwhelmed any attempts to create what could be called actual group feeling. In the next two experiments a group factor was introduced by recruiting natural groups. This technique provides the opportunity of having a variable that modifies the group of individuals in a more marked manner than the stimulating and arousing characteristics of the experimental condition itself. This technique does, however, have the shortcoming that the experimenters cannot predictably control the intensity of the previous relationships between the members of the group.

"Friends" and "Strangers"

In the third study, consequently, we recruited natural groups. We did this by advertising for groups of four people to come to the laboratory at one time, one person taking the responsibility for recruiting the three others. In this manner, subjects brought their friends to the experiment. These groups ("friends") could then be compared with groups of individually recruited subjects ("strangers"). Furthermore, we modified the experimental procedure so as to observe the effect of deviating without the possibility of conforming. To do this, we initially flashed a series of slides in which the subject supposedly performed the judgmental task first, and then the group either agreed or disagreed. After this initial series, the subject went last, as in the original conformity experiment, and the group either conformed to or deviated from the correct answer to the stimulus. For each of the conditions, group-recruited and individual-recruited, we had two different conditions when the subject went first. In one, the answers of the other subjects always conformed to the subject's, and in another, the others disagreed with him 80 per cent of the time.

TABLE 3

Effect of Attitudes of Friends and Strangers on Group Mean FFA Level

| | FFA level (μEq/L) | | | | |
Condition	Sample 1	Sample 2	Sample 3	Sample 4	Sample 5
Strangers, agree	1038	888	857	1066	878
Strangers, disagree	909	710	885	945	927
Friends, agree	714	603	751	746	815
Friends, disagree	672	598	728	775	821

Blood samples in sequence.

The results indicate that differences at the beginning of the experiment may be related to the method of recruitment. The plasma FFA levels at the time of initial puncture and at rest were lower in the natural groups than in the individually recruited subjects (Table 3). Further, conformity was significantly higher in the natural groups than in the individually recruited conditions ($F = 8.75$, $p < .001$). When the group was made up of "strangers," the plasma FFA increases were greater in the individuals who were accepted as leaders when in the non-leadership situation. This is comparable to the results observed in the first study (where all the subjects were individually recruited and therefore "strangers") in that the greatest increases in plasma FFA level occurred in the high-cohesive, better-ability subjects. When the group was made up of "friends," plasma FFA levels did not rise when the subject was a leader, but, in contrast, did increase significantly when the subject was not reinforced as a leader (Table 4). We have interpreted these data as demonstrating that in a natural group among "friends," the assumption of leadership is not of itself a strongly arousing factor, but that the element which does become important is the agreement or the disagreement that then ensues among one's friends. If the group of "friends" thinks the same as oneself, one relaxes, and there is hardly any change in FFA level. However, if the group disagrees, there is a steep rise in FFA.

TABLE 4

Effect of Friends and Strangers on Mean Group FFA Changes during Leadership

Condition	$\dfrac{\text{Sample 4 FFA} - \text{Sample 3 FFA}}{\text{Sample 2 FFA}} \times 100$
Strangers, agree	15.0
Strangers, disagree	10.2
Friends, agree	0.3
Friends, disagree	9.2

A similar contrast is shown in the pattern of FFA changes during the conformity period. The plasma FFA level decreased during this period for the groups of "strangers." This would indicate that when a subject in an individually recruited group makes his judgmental decision after everyone else, he no longer is aroused by his responsibilities to the group. In fact, those subjects who did not conform at all (i.e., those who completely ignored the group) showed a greater decline in plasma FFA level than those who conformed even slightly. The reverse was observed for the subjects recruited as a group. For those groups of "friends," during the conformity situation a consistent rise in plasma FFA levels occurred. However, those subjects who conformed most did have smaller increases than those who conformed least. In this situation, the reference point seems to be the group interaction, instead of the individual stimulus, and the greatest degree of arousal for the individual depends upon how much the person deviates from the group.

This study suggested that the degree of autonomic activity could be modified by the condition of interaction between the members of the groups. The resting FFA level could distinguish between a group that is created during the experimental period and a previously existing group. This difference in autonomic activity permits inferences about the meaning of "group" and "cohesion" under the two circumstances. It is useful to compare this study with the first one on cohesion and ability. In this study an attempt was made to create high cohesion by experimental instructions. In this case being the best performer in the groups created by the experimenters produced stress, just as being agreed with and pushed into a leadership position became stressful among the "strangers." The contrasting results in the groups who came to the laboratory already existing as a natural group indicated that there is greater emphasis upon agreement among friends than upon the success of the performance. Previous studies of experimentally created cohesion have frequently shown that cohesion could predict conformity and other effects in experimentally created as well as in natural groups. The additional physiological dimension gives indications that a different mechanism is operating in each condition. The use of natural groups in the laboratory results in the loss of a certain amount of control, since previous interaction cannot be equated. But this procedure may be necessary in order to produce group conditions rather than individual activity within a group context. The change in plasma FFA levels suggests that either creating a group out of previously non-grouped individuals or attempting to disrupt a pre-existing group will cause the most marked degree of autonomic activation.

Leadership and Agreement

In the last study to be reported here we investigated whether accepted and rejected leadership has an impact on FFA level. All groups were recruited as groups. Group identification was heightened by promising an extra reward to the best-performing group. During the trial period all subjects were put into leadership position by the following method. The individual subject was last in the order of making a judgment; however, the subjects were told that after this initial decision each subject could change his answer if he so desired, and, in a programmed manner, the opinions of "everybody else" always changed toward the individual subject. That is, although the "others" might initially have disagreed with him, eventually they ended up agreeing with him, which was giving the subject an impression of being acclaimed as a leader. In these studies we were interested not so much in conformity as in the subject's further relation to the group. Hence, in the final phase of the experiment the subject became the first person to answer. In one condition, the group disagreed with the subject most of the time, and in another condition, they agreed with him. In addition, there were two types of task difficulty. One condition used lines as stimulus slides similar to the type employed by Asch (Jackson and Saltzstein, 1956), which are easy to define; the other used a visual maze developed by Jackson (Keys et al., 1954), which is very difficult to solve. For our present purpose the critical time phase in this study is the last period, at which time we can see the difference in the amount of responsibility the person has for the group (Table 5). Where the task is easy, the amount of disagreement on the part of "others" makes little difference, for there is little rise in the plasma FFA levels. However, where the task is difficult (the visual maze) there is a slight decline in plasma FFA level if everybody agrees, and if the leadership is rejected there is a significant increase in plasma FFA level.

TABLE 5

Change in FFA Level during Last Leadership Period

Condition	FFA (μEq/L)
Easy, agree	31
Easy, disagree	42
Difficult, agree	−1
Difficult, disagree	80

Summary and Conclusions

Embarking, as we did, from two points of departure—the impact of sociology upon medicine, on the one hand, and the potential usefulness of physiological responses to experimental sociology, on the other—we may best summarize the lessons we have learned from those very same points. First, it appears well established that the specific characteristics of group interaction do modify differentially the physiological responses of our subjects. From the fact that even within the confines of the laboratory sociological forces have turned out to be significant determinants of the process of lipid mobilization, we may reasonably conclude that eventually the epidemiologic observations concerning disease may be tested experimentally. This link between the clinical observations and those of the laboratory is still in the initial stages of development. Second, there are some general conclusions to be drawn about the sociological variables of pressure to conform, leadership, and group membership. We may say, for example, that if the social situation is perceived simply as a background to individual achievement, the dominant variable will be the potential for individual achievement and its meaning. In this situation, pressure to conform and pressure to assume leadership may be viewed as arousing stimuli, and the individual may seek to avoid these situations. If, however, the group relationship has the dominant meaning, the performance of the task may be seen in terms of the group interaction, and then deviation from the group norm becomes the arousing condition. Conforming behavior is then attended by decreased arousal.

Third, and finally, these studies have demonstrated that the marked variability between individuals makes it necessary that the experimenters fully understand the specific meaning that the experimental condition holds for the subjects. Furthermore, it has become quite apparent that group relationships may provide either arousing or reassuring connotations for the individual, and that only by the simultaneous measurement of a physiological variable can we successfully identify exactly what response the stimulus evokes.

REFERENCES

Asch, S. E. Studies of independence and conformity: a minority of one against a unanimous majority. *Psychol. Monogr.*, 1956, **70**, No. 9.

Back, K. W. Influence through social communication. *J. abnorm. soc. Psychol.*, 1951, **46**, 9–26.

Back, K. W., Bogdonoff, M. D., Shaw, D. M., and Klein, R. F. An interpretation of experimental conformity through physiological measures. *Behav. Sci.*, 1963, **8**, 34–40.

Bogdonoff, M. D. The relationship of central nervous system activity to lipid metabolism. *A.M.A. Arch. intern. Med.*, 1960, **105**, 505–9.

Bogdonoff, M. D., Estes, E. H., Jr., and Trout, D. L. Acute effect of psychologic stimuli upon plasma non-esterified fatty acid levels. *Proc. Soc. Exp. Biol. Med.*, 1959, **100**, 503–4.

Bogdonoff, M. D., Estes, E. H., Jr., Harlan, P. R., Trout, D. L., and Kirshner, N. Metabolic and cardiovascular changes during a state of acute central nervous system arousal. *J. clin. Endocrin. Metab.*, 1960a, **20**, 1333–39.

Bogdonoff, M. D., Weissler, A. M., and Merritt, F. L. The effect of autonomic ganglionic blockade upon serum free fatty acid levels in man. *J. clin. Invest.*, 1960b, **39**, 959–65.

Bogdonoff, M. D., Estes, E. H., Jr., Friedberg, S. J., and Klein, R. F. Fat mobilization in man. *Ann. intern. Med.*, 1961a, **55**, 328–38.

Bogdonoff, M. D., Linhart, J. W., Klein, R. F., and Estes, E. H., Jr. The specific structure of compounds effecting fat mobilization in man. *J. clin.
Invest.*, 1961b, **40**, 1993–96.

Bogdonoff, M. D., Back, K. W., Klein, R. F., Estes, E. H., Jr., and Nichols,
C. R. The physiologic response to conformity pressure in man. *Ann. intern.
Med.*, 1962, **57**, 389–97.

Brehm, M. L., Back, K. W., and Bogdonoff, M. D. A physiological effect of
cognitive dissonance under stress and deprivation. *J. abnorm. soc. Psychol.*,
1964, **69**, 303–10.

Crutchfield, R. S. Conformity and character. *Amer. Psychologist*, 1955, **10**,
191–98.

Dole, V. P. A relation between non-esterified fatty acids in plasma and the
metabolism of glucose. *J. clin. Invest.*, 1956, **35**, 150–54.

Friedberg, S. J., Harlan, W. R., Trout, D. L., and Estes, E. H., Jr. The effect
of exercise on the concentration and turnover of plasma non-esterified fatty
acids. *J. clin. Invest.*, 1960, **39**, 215–20.

Friedman, M., and Rosenman, R. A. Association of specific overt behavior
pattern with blood and cardiovascular findings, blood cholesterol level,
blood clotting time, incidence of arcus senilis and clinical coronary artery
disease. *J. Amer. Med. Ass.*, 1959, **169**, 1286–96.

Gerard, H. B. Disagreement with others, their credibility and experienced
stress. *J. abnorm. soc. Psychol.*, 1961, **62**, 554–64.

Gofman, J. W., Jones, H. B., Lyon, T. P., Lindgren, F. T., Strisower, B., Col-
man, D., and Herring, V. Blood lipids and human atherosclerosis. *Circulation*, 1952, **5**, 119–34.

Jackson, J. M., and Saltzstein, H. B. Group membership on conformity processes. Ann Arbor, Mich., Research Center for Group Dynamics, 1956.

Kannel, W. B., Dawber, T. R., Kagan, A., Revotskie, N., and Stokes, J., III.
Factors of risk in the development of coronary heart disease—six-year fol-
low-up experience. The Framingham Study. *Ann. intern. Med.*, 1961, **55**,
33–50.

Keys, A., Fidanza, F., Scardi, V., Bergami, G., Keys, M. H., and di Lorenzo, F.
Studies on serum cholesterol and other characteristics of clinically healthy
men in Naples. *A.M.A. Arch. intern. Med.*, 1954, **93**, 328–36.

Morris, J. N. Occupation and coronary heart disease. *A.M.A. Arch. intern.
Med.*, 1959, **104**, 903–7.

Thomas, C. B., and Murphy, E. A. Further studies on cholesterol levels in the
Johns Hopkins medical students: the effect of stress at examinations. *J.
chron. Dis.*, 1958, **8**, 661–68.

Wertlake, P. T., Wilcox, A. A., Haley, M. I., and Peterson, J. E. Relationship
of mental and emotional stress to serum cholesterol levels. *Proc. Soc. Exp.
Biol. Med.*, 1958, **97**, 163–65.

Wolf, S. Cardiovascular reactions to symbolic stimuli. *Circulation*, 1958, **18**,
287–92.

Physiological Measurement in Social Psychological Research

HAROLD B. GERARD*
Bell Telephone Laboratories, Murray Hill, New Jersey

In recent years, social psychologists have become increasingly interested in using physiological measures in their research (see, for example, Burdick and Burnes, 1958; Cooper, 1959; Hokanson and Burgess, 1962). Two trends are responsible for this interest. One is a growing dissatisfaction with total reliance upon the verbal reports of subjects; the other is a developing concern with intra-individual processes.

Many experiments in social psychology rely completely upon the subject's phenomenology to determine the degree of success of the induction of an experimental variable, the presence of some intervening process, and the final effect predicted by the hypothesis being tested. Verbal reports, checklists, and rating scales are used in some experiments as measures of the independent, intervening, and dependent variables. Often, in collecting such data, experimenters do not adhere to the natural sequence of events in time. The success of the manipulation of the independent variable is typically measured at the very end of the experiment. Occasionally, this is unavoidable. For instance, in experiments where attraction to another person is manipulated, it is awkward to ask the subject at the beginning of the experimental session, immediately after the experimental variable has been induced, how attractive he found the others. Many experimental variables, like inter-personal attraction, are difficult to manipulate. Any attempt to measure the subject's attitudes or feeling at the time they are presumed to be guiding his overt behavior might well make him self-conscious, solicitous, or even recalcitrant.

* Present address: University of California, Riverside.

Suppose that we had just induced some level of fear in a subject. If we asked him how emotional he felt at that moment, he might suddenly become self-conscious about his feelings. He might then ask himself if, considering the situation, it is "proper" that he be as calm or as worked-up as he is. *Ought* he to be feeling what he does? Perhaps a desire to be consistent with his answer to another question or rating scale might prompt him to misrepresent what he actually feels. Another reaction to the question might be an attempt to guess what the experimenter wants him to feel; he may have a strong altruistic desire to help the experimenter confirm what he assumes to be the experimenter's hypothesis. If the subject were in a devilish mood, he might want to thwart the experimenter's attempts. Anyone who has handled a large number of laboratory subjects is aware of these and other kinds of perversity. Self-conciousness, self-queries, and attempts to outguess the experimenter undoubtedly interfere with the processes that really concern the experimenter. To solve this problem, we often try to misrepresent the purpose of an experiment to a subject. However, I suspect that we frequently fail and often make the subject suspicious.

The possibility of negative results prompts us to measure the independent variables. When our hypothesis has not been confirmed by the data, we want assurance that the conditions necessary for testing the hypothesis were in fact created. Taking measurements of the independent variables at the end of an experiment, which is usually done, is a very uncomfortable compromise, since the events subsequent to the experimental induction of these variables tend to affect the subject's response to any later measurement. The measurement, then, may not truly reflect the level of the variable at the time it was induced. In a social-influence experiment some years ago (Gerard, 1954) I varied both the subject's attraction to the group and the discrepancy between his opinion and that of the other group members. The final check on the manipulation of attraction showed a difference between the manipulated levels; but it also showed a strong interaction with opinion discrepancy. The closer the subject's final opinion was to that of the others, the more attracted he was to the others.

In addition to these problems, social psychologists have the pervasive problem of evaluating verbal responses when one subject's response is to be compared with the response of another, that is, the problem of establishing inter-subject equivalence of meaning for the various points on a verbal-response measurement scale. An entire field of psychological measurement has developed around this problem. At present, few solutions can be offered the psychologist whose primary focus is on the content of psychological processes. Similar issues, in a somewhat different guise, dog the experimenter in evaluating physiological response data. However, with physiological measures, there is greater opportunity for establishing prior baseline response measures for a given subject. However, there are problems here, too, since patterns of physiological response to similar stimuli have been shown to vary from subject to subject.

Social psychology is becoming more individual-oriented, which may also account for the growing interest in physiological measurement. Ten years ago, when some of us thought in terms of group concepts, such as cohesiveness, pressures toward uniformity, status, group decisions, and group problem-solving, a distinction between social psychology and individual psychology came easily. Now many active experimentalists frame their questions in terms of individual motivational and cognitive functioning, and the distinction is becoming less and less clear. Much of this current work has been generated by a cognitively oriented approach in which the underlying dynamic is the reduction of tension produced by inconsistency (Heider, 1958; Festinger, 1957; Brehm and Cohen, 1962). In a sense, this approach is a return to the orientation of the thirties and early forties, when social psychologists were studying aspects of individual motivation and suggestion (see, for example, the work of Asch, 1940). In line with the interest then, there were some notable attempts to study the physiological effects of social confrontations on the individual, one of which I shall presently discuss in some detail.

Given this interest in psychological tension, and given that any psychological event must have a neurological correlate, it seems natural to attempt to measure physiological responses which might be among the concomitants, like autonomic arousal. Presumably an intervening process of tension build-up should be accompanied by some autonomic discharge.

Physiological data, or any additional data, for that matter, may help us to select alternative interpretations of the results of an experiment. Suppose that in some experiment we find evidence for more cognitive work in one condition than in another, as indicated by a greater change in some attitude in the first condition. This difference is due, we may have originally hypothesized, to the production in the first condition of factors requiring change, namely, greater inconsistency and concomitant tension. On the other hand, the difference in attitude change may be due to the first condition's having facilitated change by making it easier for the subject to reduce his original attitude commitment. Without other data or further research, it is impossible to choose the more tenable of the two theories. Presumably, if the first process accounted for the change, subjects in the condition in which more change occurred should show greater physiological arousal prior to the change than subjects in the other condition. On the other hand, if the facilitation hypothesis is more tenable, the reverse would be true; at least those subjects in the condition showing more attitude change should not show more arousal. Taking a measurement of arousal during the period prior to the attitude change might enable us to place greater confidence in one or the other interpretation.

I am not suggesting that social psychologists should suddenly forsake traditional verbal and behavioral measurement techniques. However, tapping the subject's psychological tension level may provide useful supplementary data. Different degrees of tension should be reflected by corresponding levels of autonomic arousal. If we can demonstrate that the end effect predicted by the theory (an effect such as a change of attitude, a conforming response to group pressure, or an increase in affiliation) was preceded by differential states of arousal, we can better establish a more convincing case for a particular hypothesis. Such gauging of the intervening process with physiological measurement is not absolutely necessary, since, if the prediction is confirmed, support is lent to the theory being tested. However, responses that reflect some intervening process may help us either to rule out alternative interpretations or to reinterpret the data if the original hypothesis is disconfirmed.

At this point I want to state what has already been implicit in this discussion. The measurement of physiological arousal is intended only to detect a state of psychological stress; it does not enable us to put a label on the state. Given our present knowledge of autonomic functioning in different psychological states, it is impossible to work backward and identify the state from a knowledge of the physiology. Hence, on the basis of the physiological data alone, we cannot label the subject's state as fear, anger, or joy. We can say only that he is aroused. However, the stimulus situation confronting him, and other response data, may, when taken together, justify giving a psychological label to the underlying state or process.

An example from the past, and some of my own recent research, will illustrate how physiological measurement can be used. In 1936, C. E. Smith ran an experiment and obtained results amazingly similar to some findings in my own recent work. Even though Smith's experiment was designed nearly 30 years ago, it fits the paradigm of much current research on conformity, both in the problem investigated and in the method used. Several weeks before the experimental session, the subjects in Smith's experiment were administered a set of 20 opinion items in their classroom. For each item, they indicated their agreement or disagreement, and also, on a 5-point scale, the intensity of their conviction. Items such as "the Soviet experiment in government should be encouraged," "it should be considered bad form for women to drink alcoholic beverages," "modernistic art should be enthusiastically encouraged," and "socialism and communism are valuable balance wheels in our political life and should receive full protection," were considered controversial opinions in those days. Four weeks later, each subject was asked to participate in an experiment. Subjects were run either by Henry Murray or by Donald McKinnon. Smith wanted to determine the amount of stress experienced by the subject when he was in agreement and when he was in disagreement with the opinion item, and when he was *with* and when he was *against* the majority of his peers. For 10 of the items, the subject was given a fictitious majority opinion that agreed with his own, whereas on the remaining 10 items he found himself in disagreement with this fictitious majority. Smith allocated the 20 items into two groups of 10 such that for each subject the groups of items were matched for the degree of conviction the subject had originally expressed in them.

A Wechsler psychogalvanometer was used to measure skin resistance changes. Smith found a positive correlation between the amount of autonomic reactivity the subject showed when presented with an item and his degree of initial conviction in agreeing or disagreeing

with the item, regardless of whether or not his opinion coincided with
that of the majority. This relationship, however, did not hold for items
on which the subjects had expressed an extreme degree of conviction
(point 5 on the conviction scale). Subjects also consistently tended
to be more reactive to items with which they disagreed than to items
with which they agreed. The effects were more marked when the subject was *against* the majority than when he was *with* them. Smith gave
a very modern interpretation of the results, that is, an interpretation
which, with some slight changes in language, would be indistinguish-
able from the present cognitive approach to this kind of problem. He
suggested that three processes were operating: intensity of conviction, which tends to fortify the individual against possible disagreement (since the issues were controversial); a decision, which implies
a choice of going with or against the group; and an assertion, which
involves committing oneself to agreement or disagreement publicly
(to the experimenter). Smith interprets the lack of reactivity displayed by the subject to an opinion held with the most extreme level
of conviction as an indication that the subject had probably convinced himself so firmly of his view that actual or potential arguments did not challenge the opinion. Thus, by previously considering
counterarguments, he had reduced dissonance, so to speak, and could
now easily dismiss arguments that might contradict his opinion.

In an experiment done 25 years later (Gerard, 1961), I unwittingly
repeated Smith's experiment in a somewhat different form, and got
essentially the same results. By then, Asch (1952) had given us his
lines and a technique for confronting the individual with a majority
judgment regarding these lines. In Asch's procedure, the subject is
asked to match one of three lines of different lengths with a single
line; he finds that on most of the trials in the sequence his judgment
disagrees with that of a group of peers, who are actually accomplices
of the experimenter. I had earlier devised a situation in which four
subjects could be run simultaneously. Each of the four subjects is in
the same parallel situation and is given false information about the
judgments of the other three subjects. By being given appropriate
false information, each subject is led to believe that he disagrees with
the three others on most of the judgments. The experiment was designed to study the effect of the subject's estimate of his own ability
relative to the ability of the other three subjects, on the ease with

which he could reconcile his disagreement with them. Given that the subject cannot change his opinion, to the extent that the disagreement is upsetting to him he will attempt to account for the difference of opinion or to explain it away. There are many ways the subject may do this. One of these is to conclude that his ability to form the opinion differs markedly from the ability of others. If, in an experiment, the subject is provided with knowledge of an ability difference at the outset, he should then have little difficulty in coming to terms with a difference of opinion with the others, whereas if he believes himself to be equal to the others in ability, this avenue of resolving the difference of opinion would be closed to him and we should expect him to experience difficulty. These expectations were not confirmed by the data; had I not taken skin resistance measurements, I would have had difficulty in giving a plausible *post hoc* interpretation of the findings. But let me get to the specifics.

Different self-ability estimates were induced experimentally on a prior visual judgment task by giving the subject a false performance score on the prior task. One-third of the subjects were led to believe that they had performed better than the others, one-third that they were about equal to the others, and one-third that they were poorer than the others. As stated above, I predicted that a subject whose ability was equal to that of the others would experience greater difficulty in accounting for the disagreement in opinion than a subject whose ability was either superior or inferior to that of the others. The test situation was arranged so that the subject could not yield his opinion to the majority. This enforced deviation was accomplished by having all four subjects respond simultaneously. Each subject found himself in disagreement with the majority for most of the trials in the sequence (on a few of the trials, the fictitious majority made correct judgment). On the critical trials, half the subjects were exposed to a large discrepancy in judgment with the others, whereas the other half confronted only a relatively small discrepancy. Thus, within the same basic situation, three levels of relative ability were manipulated, and within each ability level there were two degrees of judgmental discrepancy.

As I hinted earlier, the findings were much the same as those of Smith. Smith found a positive relationship between autonomic reactivity and depth of conviction. I found a positive relationship between reactivity and the subject's self-ability estimate. In view of certain other questionnaire data, it is fairly safe to assume that the self-ability manipulation varied the subject's depth of conviction in his subsequent judgments. The relationship between ability and reactivity was strengthened when the subject found himself confronted with a large as compared with a small judgment discrepancy. The reactivity data, changes in base-level skin conductance, are shown in Table 1. The figures indicate the change during the first nine and also during the last nine judgments on the three levels of relative ability and on the two levels of disagreement. During the first nine judgments, we see a linear relationship between the increase in conductance and the subject's ability ($p < .01$ by an F test). There is a continued increase for the second set of nine judgments in the large-discrepancy condition ($p < .01$), but it levels off when the judgmental discrepancy is small. In order to examine certain attitudinal correlates of deviation from the group, questionnaire data were collected during the experiment. These data enabled us to determine whether the subject's evaluations of his own ability and the ability of others, and his guess as to their evaluation of him, were consistent with one another. In line with the prediction about the ease of coming to terms with deviation, I expected that when the subject believed that he was equal to the others in ability he would show more inconsistency than when he believed that he was better or poorer than they. Instead, the degree of this consistency was inversely related to the self-ability levels. Hence we see that autonomic arousal and attitudinal consistency are both related to the ability manipulation. Both sets of data indicate that when the subject's ability is greater than that of the others, he finds the disagreement with the others psychologically more stressful.

TABLE 1

Change in Base Level of Skin Conductance in Micromhos

		Small discrepancy		Large discrepancy	
Ability of others relative to self		1st series change	2nd series change	1st series change	2nd series change
Less	−	+3.55	+0.48	+3.00	+2.47
Equal	0	+2.73	+1.62	+1.67	+1.44
Greater	+	+1.97	+1.41	+1.38	+1.47

An increase in conductance indicates greater arousal.

There was a fundamental difference between the majority confrontation in this experiment and that in Smith's study. Before asking the subject to state his own opinion, Smith indicated to him the majority's stand on the issue. Smith could manipulate agreement and disagreement easily, since he already knew the subject's opinion from the previous questionnaire. Thus, if the trial were selected as one in which the subject was to be in agreement with the majority, and the subject had originally agreed with the opinion statement, he was told that the majority agreed with the statement. If the item was to be one on which the subject disagreed with the majority, he was told that the majority had disagreed with the opinion statement. However, Smith could not prevent the subject from changing his opinion. In my study, the subject was confronted with a *fait accompli* in the judgment at hand. He stated his opinion before he learned the judgment of the majority, since everyone responded simultaneously and then saw each other's judgments. Thus, there could be no decision to go with or against the group. The advantage of my procedure over Smith's was that I had complete control of the subject's behavior, whereas Smith did not. The problem I was studying amounted to observing the subject's reaction to finding that he was a minority of one. If the subject had been allowed to change his judgment when he learned the majority's choice, I would have confronted the same subject self-selection problem Smith had. That is, those subjects who remained in disagreement might be quite different in certain unknown respects from those who yielded. Being aware of the limitations imposed by his procedure, Smith made some rather uninformative subanalyses for those subjects who did change their opinion when confronted by majority disagreement. Still, my procedure failed to capture the important element of decision involved in agreeing or disagreeing with a group. The two studies are, therefore, not quite comparable in what they were studying.

In the next experiment (Gerard, 1960) I developed a technique that promised to capture this element of decision and yet maintain complete control of the subject's behavior. As in the Smith study, the subject was confronted on each trial with a two-alternative choice situation. Each stimulus consisted of two multi-pointed stars projected side by side on a screen for one-fifth of a second. The subject's task was to choose the star with the greater number of points. Fifteen such

star pairs were presented; by being given false performance feedback, the subject was led to believe that he was either very good or
very poor at making this type of judgment. Confidence and decision-
time data collected on each trial left very little doubt about the success of this ability manipulation. After the first series of judgments,
the subject was told the following:

We are interested not only in your considered judgments, but in your first
impulses, since we believe that certain important phenomena are linked to
one's first impulses in a situation of this kind. The responses you have just
made have conditioned your forearm muscles to act when you have made a
choice. That is, the nerve pathways from your brain to your forearm will
energize your forearm muscles. We can pick up this implicit muscle movement
with some very sensitive electromyograph equipment which amplifies the minute muscle potentials generated in your forearm. The electrodes attached to
your forearm [these were dummy EKG electrodes, which were fixed in place
immediately after the ability induction] enable us to do this. Keep both arms
perfectly still, since we want only the implicit muscle movements to operate
the lamps on your panel. We will also be measuring your skin resistance with
the electrodes attached to your hand, since we are interested in other physiological reactions too.

He was then told, "Since we thought you would like to see the
others' judgments, we will let you see their first-impulse choices on
your lamp panel. Each one of you will be assigned a number, either
1, 2, or 3, since for various reasons we don't want your personal
identity revealed during the experiment. Under your panel you will
find an envelope with a card in it containing your number." In actu-
ality, each subject was assigned the number 3 and each assumed that
the others were 1 and 2. There were only three subjects used in this
experiment. The instructions continued, "During any given trial,
your impulse may have switched from the right to the left forearm
and back again perhaps several times. However, the impulse that
occurs immediately after your green respond light comes on will be
displayed on your own and the others' panels. If you are subject 1,
your impulse will appear on the first row on each panel. The responses
of subjects 2 and 3 will appear in the second and third rows." In actu-
ality, the display for all three rows was pre-programmed to produce
apparent conformity or apparent deviation. The star-pairs used for
this second series were quite easy to discriminate. For the first seven
trials, everyone was treated identically. On trials 1, 2, and 3, the
prearranged program indicated that everyone's first impulse was to

choose the correct star. On trial 4, subject 1 chose the incorrect star, while 2 and 3 chose the correct one. On trial 5, everyone, including the subject himself, was correct again. On trials 6 and 7, subjects 1 and 2 were *both* wrong, while 3 (the actual subject, of course) was correct. On trial 8, the separation occurred. The subject assigned to the conformer condition found that his first impulse was to choose the incorrect star, along with the other two subjects, whereas the deviate chose the correct star. From trial 8 on, the conformer chose the same star as subjects 1 and 2, regardless of whether or not the others were correct. The deviate, on the other hand, made the physically correct choice, regardless of the others' choices. Subjects 1 and 2 were always in agreement, right or wrong. After 18 trials, the conformer–deviate induction was considered complete.

We found, as Smith did, that the subject with greater initial confidence in his judgments, the high-ability subject, showed greater reactivity than the low-ability subject when he conformed as well as when he deviated. This evidence and evidence from some of my more recent research suggests that the high-ability subject confronted a greater challenge. We also find that under the conformity induction, the high-ability subject justified his behavior by increasing his attraction to the others, whereas under the deviate induction, he justified his behavior by rejecting them.

In another study just completed, I manipulated the *fait accompli* character of the situation during the false first-impulse series by presenting the first-impulse judgments of the subject and the other either sequentially, as in the study just reported, or simultaneously, as in the line-judgment experiment. As predicted, greater reactivity is shown in the sequential presentation, where there is a decision to go against the majority.

So far I have discussed instances where skin conductance was used to detect intervening processes after the induction of experimental variables. In some work that followed up findings reported by Schachter (1959) in his study of bases for social affiliation, I used physiological measurement to check on the induction of experimental variables. In a study (Gerard and Rabbie, 1961) which attempted to reproduce the basic situation that Schachter used, I induced two levels of fear. Within each fear level were conditions in which the subject was or was not told the emotional level of three other people anticipating the same circumstances, namely, receiving electric shock. The hypothesis being tested, which derives from Festinger's (1954) theory of social comparison, was that given increasing amounts of information about the others' reactions, the subject would show less affiliation. Affiliation was measured by the subject's desire to be with the other victims prior to being shocked. I used physiological measurement to check on the success of the induction of the two levels of fear. When the subject was threatened with a severe shock there was a greater increase in basal conductance than when he was threatened with a weak shock. Verbal report corroborated this difference. Together, these data gave me confidence in the success with which the levels of fear had been manipulated. The affiliation data, however, did not entirely support the social-comparison hypothesis. I also discovered an interaction between sex, birth order, and autonomic reactivity in response to the threat of shock. First-born females showed greater reactivity than later-born females, whereas first-born males showed less reactivity than later-born males. First-born females also showed more affiliation than later-born, the reverse being true for males.

In a second experiment (Gerard, 1963) I varied the uncertainty of the subject's own emotional state in order to examine the social-comparison hypothesis more directly. Assuming that the greater the uncertainty experienced by the person about his worked-up body state, the greater would be his desire for social-comparison information, I predicted that the greater the uncertainty, the greater the affiliation would be. Uncertainty was manipulated by presenting the subject with what he believed to be his emotionality level on a meter display in front of him. Finger-electrodes and an EKG electrode were attached to the subject, and he was told that this paraphernalia would enable us to measure his emotionality level. He could see momentary changes in his own emotionality on his meter, which was ostentatiously labeled "emotionality index." For the high-uncertainty induction, the subject received information which showed his emotionality level to be very variable, averaging about 75. For the low-uncertainty treatment, the subject was presented with a relatively steady meter reading, which again averaged about 75. During the three-minute period in which this faked emotionality index was being presented, a continuous recording was made of each subject's skin resistance. We computed the variability of his skin resistance as measured arbitrarily at ten-second intervals from the beginning to the end of the induction. The data showed a greater variability of these measurements under the high- than under the low-uncertainty treatment. Variations in reactivity were apparently induced with variations of a fictitiously fluctuating meter needle. I did not analyze the data to determine whether or not physiological changes actually tracked the meter display, since I was interested only in obtaining evidence of the successful induction of differential uncertainty. The subject's verbal report, obtained at the very end of the experiment, showed only a slight, insignificant difference in uncertainty between the two levels. The physiological measure of uncertainty was taken at the time the variable was being induced, whereas the verbal-report data were taken long after the induction. The small residual difference in uncertainty between the treatments in the verbal-report measure was due, possibly, to the effects of the intervening events. If the physiological measure had not been taken, there would have been little ground for examining the relationship between affiliation and uncertainty, since there would be no evidence that differential uncertainty had indeed been induced. The data provide some support for the social-comparison hypothesis in that there was greater affiliation under high than under low uncertainty.

In a very recent study, I examined physiological accompaniments of the decision process as a dependent variable. Dissonance theory (Festinger, 1957) predicts that after a choice the chosen alternative will increase in value relative to the non-chosen one. This effect is assumed to be mediated by certain unpleasant implications of the choice, which produce the psychological tension referred to as dissonance. The unpleasant implications are that the decision has precluded the person's enjoyment of the positive features of the non-chosen alternative, and/or has forced him to suffer the consequences attendant upon possessing the undesirable features of the chosen one, or has had both these effects. Naturally, the greater the number of qualities the two alternatives have in common, the less will be the dissonance, since choosing either will not preclude enjoying qualities of the other. If this cognitive overlap is held constant, the more nearly equal in value the choice alternatives are, the more difficult will be the choice and the greater will be this post-decisional dissonance.

This tension is presumably experienced phenomenally by the person as regret. This view of the effects of a decision should lead to a prediction of greater physiological arousal *after*, rather than before, the decision. The arousal should be the greater, the closer in value the choice alternatives are.

In the experiment I used finger-pulse amplitude as a measure. After the subject had evaluated twelve paintings according to how much he liked them, a photoplethysmograph was fixed in place at the tip of his index finger on the side opposite the fingernail. This probe is a small block of Bakelite, 1 in. × ¾ in. × ½ in., containing a grain-of-wheat light bulb that shines into the fingertip, and a small photocell, the output of which is fed through a bridge circuit and amplified. With this device it is possible to detect minute changes in the amount of blood in the fingertip capillary bed, since the amount of light reflected back to the photocell is inversely proportional to the amount of blood in these vessels. Thus, pulse rate as well as pulse amplitude can be measured. When a stressor is applied to the subject, a constriction of the arterioles occurs, which is detectable four or five pulse beats after the stressor. This appears as a decrease in the amplitude envelope of the pulse beats. The details of the physiology are described by Davis, Buchwald, and Frankmann (1955). If maximum dissonance occurs immediately after a decision, we would expect to observe a decrease in pulse amplitude shortly after the decision.

After the probe was hooked up, the subject was asked to choose one of two paintings, each of which was projected on a separate screen in front and to either side of him. He was told that he could have as a gift a print of the one he chose. Two conditions were run, one in which the third- and the fourth-ranked paintings (as evaluated by the subject previously) were paired, and another in which the third- and the eighth-ranked ones were paired. Table 2 presents the data from the twelve subjects in the close-value condition and from the eleven subjects in the disparate-value condition. The finger-pulse amplitude for each time period was taken as the average of a number of pulse beats during each of the periods. Proportionate changes are indicated from each period to the next. The important comparison for us is the difference between the two conditions in the change from immediately before to immediately after the decision. Ten subjects show some constriction in the close-value condition, whereas

TABLE 2

Finger-Pulse Amplitude Changes during the Decision Sequence
(in mm of deflection)

Subject No.	1 Rest	$\frac{2-1}{1}$	2 Pre	$\frac{3-2}{2}$	3 Immed Pre	4 Immed Post	$\frac{4-3}{3}$	5 Post	$\frac{5-4}{4}$
				Close-Value Condition					
1F	6.0	.00	6.0	−.08	5.5	4.5	−.18	5.0	+.11
2F	9.0	+.06	9.5	.00	9.5	6.5	−.32	7.0	+.08
3M	3.0	−.50	2.0	+.25	2.5	2.5	.00	4.0	+.60
4F	30.0	+.02	30.5	−.13	26.5	16.0	−.36	32.0	+1.00
5F	53.0	−.16	44.0	−.30	31.0	24.0	−.22	52.0	+1.17
6M	35.0	−.26	26.0	−.04	25.0	23.0	−.08	36.0	+.57
7M	32.0	−.56	15.0	−.20	12.0	9.5	−.21	15.0	+.58
8M	16.5	−.09	14.0	−.36	9.0	5.5	−.39	13.5	+1.45
9F	7.0	−.28	5.0	−.10	4.5	4.0	−.11	7.0	+.75
10M	10.5	.00	10.5	−.14	9.0	8.5	−.06	11.0	+.29
11M	8.5	−.18	7.0	−.14	6.0	3.0	−.50	7.5	+1.50
12F	5.0	−.20	4.0	−.25	3.0	3.0	.00	6.0	+1.00
				Disparate-Value Condition					
1F	5.5	−.18	4.5	+.11	5.0	5.0	.00	6.0	+.20
2F	10.0	−.75	2.5	+.20	3.0	2.5	−.17	8.0	+2.20
3M	38.5	+.22	47.0	−.32	32.0	33.5	+.05	38.5	+.15
4M	25.5	.00	25.5	−.62	10.0	12.5	+.25	24.0	+.92
5M	34.5	−.06	32.0	.00	32.0	21.5	−.47	32.5	+.51
6F	22.0	−.45	12.0	−.08	11.0	11.5	+.05	17.5	+.52
7F	19.5	−.20	15.5	−.17	13.0	13.5	+.04	19.5	+.44
8M	26.5	−.34	17.5	+.09	19.0	9.0	−.52	23.5	+1.61
9M	33.5	−.40	20.0	+.17	23.5	24.0	+.02	33.0	+.38
10M	12.5	−.44	7.0	+.43	10.0	9.0	−.10	14.5	+.61
11F	12.5	.00	12.5	−.40	7.5	7.5	.00	12.5	+.67

M = male; F = female.

only four show constriction in the disparate-value condition. This study was only exploratory and is being followed up by additional research.

We have considered and given examples of the use of physiological measures to detect the presence of different levels of both independent and dependent variables and also to detect the operation of some assumed intervening process. I am convinced that this kind of measurement can be justifiably added to the armamentarium of the social psychologist. The techniques do not offer any formula for pinning a process down once and for all, nor do they substitute for even a significant fraction of the kind of data our hypotheses require us to collect. However, where a process is presumed to be occurring, and where turning the subject's attention to it would be disruptive, the measurement of a response over which the subject has little or no control (see Lykken, 1960) can at times provide the psychologist with valuable information.

REFERENCES

Asch, S. E. Studies in the principles of judgments and attitudes, II, determination of judgments by group and ego standards. *J. soc. Psychol.*, 1940, **12**, 433–65.

Asch, S. E. *Social psychology*. New York: Prentice-Hall, 1952.

Brehm, J. W., and Cohen, A. R. *Explorations in cognitive dissonance*. New York: Wiley, 1962.

Burdick, H. A., and Burnes, A. J. A test of "strain toward symmetry" theories. *J. abnorm. soc. Psychol.*, 1958, **57**, 367–70.

Cooper, J. B. Emotion in prejudice. *Science*, 1959, **130**, 314–18.

Davis, R. C., Buchwald, A. M., and Frankmann, R. W. Autonomic and muscular responses and their relation to simple stimuli. *Psychol. Monogr.*, 1955, **69**, No. 20.

Festinger, L. A theory of social comparison processes. *Hum. Relat.*, 1954, **7**, 117–40.

Festinger, L. *A theory of cognitive dissonance*. Evanston, Ill.: Row, Peterson, 1957.

Gerard, H. B. The anchorage of opinions in face-to-face groups. *Hum. Relat.*, 1954, **7**, 313–25.

Gerard, H. B. Acts, attitudes, and conformity. *Symposia Study Series No. 4, The National Institute of Social and Behavioral Science*, September 1960 *(Series Research on Social Psychology)*.

Gerard, H. B. Disagreement with others, their credibility, and experienced stress. *J. abnorm. soc. Psychol.*, 1961, **62**, 554–64.

Gerard, H. B. Emotional uncertainty and social comparison. *J. abnorm. soc. Psychol.*, 1963, **66**, 568–73.

Gerard, H. B., and Rabbie, J. M. Fear and social comparison. *J. abnorm. soc. Psychol.*, 1961, **62**, 586–92.

Heider, F. *The psychology of interpersonal relations*. New York: Wiley, 1958.

Hokanson, J. E., and Burgess, M. The effects of three types of aggression on vascular processes. *J. abnorm. soc. Psychol.*, 1962, **64**, 446–49.

Lykken, D. T. The validity of the guilty knowledge technique: the effects of faking. *J. appl. Psychol.*, 1960, **44**, 258–62.

Schachter, S. *The psychology of affiliation*. Stanford, Calif.: Stanford Univ. Press, 1959.

Smith, C. E. The autonomic excitation resulting from the interaction of individual opinion and group opinion. *J. abnorm. soc. Psychol.*, 1936, **30**, 138–64.

Muscular Tension: Physiological Activation or Psychological Act?

MURRAY HORWITZ, *New York University*

DAVID C. GLASS, *Russell Sage Foundation*

AGNES M. NIYEKAWA,* *Brooklyn College*

According to a widely held assumption, physiological arousal manifests itself in various bodily changes. Woodworth and Schlosberg (1954) list changes in skin conductance, electroencephalogram, blood pressure, heart beat, and muscle potential among the indices of level of activation. The construct "level of activation" corresponds "roughly ... to what the layman calls 'tension' or 'excitement' " (*ibid.*, p. 133), and is represented in the continuum of sleep–alertness–emotionality. It links numerous, small bodily changes to the energy mobilized in physiological functioning.

An alternative possibility, which has received scant consideration, is that these bodily processes are psychological acts. We readily conceive of large-scale bodily changes, such as running from danger, as goal-directed acts. But this conception seems to violate our presuppositions about changes that are "under the skin" and detectable only by physiological instrumentation. It may therefore seem as strange to psychologists as to laymen to treat the more rapid beating of a heart or the relaxation of a muscle after movement as a goal-directed act.

Yet such a view is not obviously incompatible with the concept of

For clarity of exposition, we present our three experiments in the reverse order from which they were actually run. The first-run experiment (Experiment III) was supported by the Office of Naval Research; the second-run (Experiment II) by the National Science Foundation and the Russell Sage Foundation; the third-run (Experiment I) by the National Science Foundation. Dr. Niyekawa collaborated with the senior author in the first-run experiment, and Dr. Glass collaborated with him in the second. Valuable assistance in running subjects was given by Louise Berenson and Eileen Toban in Experiment III, by Alfred Cohn and Seymour Giniger in Experiment II, by Roy Herrenkohl, Ira Firestone, and Joël Grinker in Experiment I. Mr. Firestone and Miss Grinker contributed, in addition, to all phases of Experiment I.
* Present address: University of Hawaii, Honolulu.

a psychological act. English and English (1958), noting the difficulty of defining an act as a unit of behavior, suggest that it "always implies a changed relationship between organism and environment" (p. 8). The directed act of running toward or away from some environmental outcome includes successively smaller bodily changes in the positioning of limbs, in muscular contraction-relaxation, in blood circulation, and so forth. One can characterize each of these, from the most molar to the most molecular, as directed toward changing the organism–environment relationship. On a purely definitional basis, none can be excluded from the domain of goal-directed acts.

Whether to include a given bodily change in the domain of goal-directed acts would seem to be an empirical rather than a definitional question. Such directed acts as pulling against a restraining harness to reach food (Miller, 1959), placing a bet (Edwards, 1962), or stating a level of aspiration (Lewin *et al.*, 1944) meet the criterion that they are functions of variables describing the relationship of the organism to its goals and avoidances. The research reported in this chapter applies the same criterion to a small, non-voluntary bodily change, namely, the relaxation of an active muscle during a pause in movement (Smith, 1953). We inquire below whether this bodily change obeys two principles that govern the intensity of goal-directed acts in general.

The first of these principles relates the intensity of an act to the attractiveness or aversiveness of its outcomes. The strength of the tendency to approach or avoid a given outcome is related by Lewin *et al.* (1944) to the positive or negative valence of the outcome, by Edwards (1962) to its subjective utility or disutility, and by Miller (1959) to its learned reward–punishment value. Despite differences in nomenclature, the variable affecting the strength of approach–avoidance tendencies seems the same. Following Lewin, we designate this variable as the valence of a goal (Va_G) when positive, and as the valence of an avoidance (Va_A) when negative.

The second principle relates the intensity of an act to the anticipation of whether the positive or negative outcome will occur. To specify the strength of approach or avoidance tendencies in given situations, Lewin and Edwards both multiply valence by the subjective probability of the outcome. Miller multiplies valence by the reciprocal of the subject's distance from the outcome; but distance, as Brunswik (quoted by Tolman, 1959, p. 103) suggests, may well be subsumed under the rubric of subjective probability. We designate the multiplier as the subjective probability of the goal (Pr_G) for an act leading to a positive outcome, or as the subjective probability of an avoidance (Pr_A) for an act leading to a negative outcome.

Finally, we designate the strength of an approach or avoidance tendency as the force toward a goal (f_G) or away from an avoidance (f_A), respectively (Lewin, 1938). Using this notation, we may summarize the foregoing principles as follows.

Assumption A. For a given act, the force toward a goal is a multiplicative function of the positive valence of the goal and the subjective probability that the act will lead to the goal:

$$f_G = F(Pr_G \times Va_G) .$$

Assumption B. For a given act, the force away from an avoidance is a multiplicative function of the negative valence of the avoidance and the subjective probability that the act will lead to the avoidance:

$$f_A = F(Pr_A \times Va_A) .$$

To apply the principles embodied in Assumptions A and B to the specific case of muscular deactivation, we employ an intuitive, mediating assumption. During a temporary pause in the performance of a motor task, an active muscle should relax the more slowly, the stronger the subject's tendency to continue toward a positive outcome (i.e., the stronger f_G) or to continue away from a negative outcome (i.e., the stronger f_A). If both approach and avoidance tendencies are present, the muscle should relax the more slowly, the greater the sum of the strengths of these tendencies (i.e., the greater $f_G + f_A$).* Level of tension (t) should thus relate to the approach–avoidance tendencies that operate during a pause in a task as follows.

Assumption C. Level of tension varies directly with the sum of the strengths of approach and avoidance forces:

$$t = F(f_G + f_A) .$$

Assumption C applies not only to approach–avoidance situations, but to pure approach situations where $f_A = 0$ and to pure avoidance situations where $f_G = 0$. Two of the experiments reported below deal

---

* In the latter case, the subject is in an approach-avoidance conflict; the assumption thus implies that relaxation is the slower, the greater the degree of conflict.

with approach–avoidance situations; the third deals with a pure approach situation. Each experiment tests specific hypotheses derived from Assumptions A, B, and C, and, in this respect, tests the general view that muscular deactivation is a goal-directed act.

Experiment I. *Tension as a Function of Success or Failure Against High- or Low-Status Competitors*

In this experiment, the subject competes with another person in performing a series of tasks. By pitting the subject against an opponent who is high or low in status, we investigate the effects of manipulating the valences of success and failure in the competition. Success should have greater positive valence against a high-status than against a low-status opponent; failure should have less negative valence against a high-status than against a low-status opponent (Chapman and Volkmann, 1939).

These relationships among the valences of success and failure should also obtain among the valences of winning and losing single trials in the series. Since each win or loss is instrumental to over-all success or failure, the positive valence of a win against a high-status opponent ($Va_{win H}$) should exceed that against a low-status opponent ($Va_{win L}$); the negative valence of a loss against a high-status opponent ($Va_{loss H}$) should be less than that against a low-status one ($Va_{loss L}$).

In summary, we have the following propositions:

Proposition 1.
$$Va_{win H} > Va_{win L} ,$$
Proposition 2.
$$Va_{loss H} < Va_{loss L} ,$$

and, by subtraction of these inequalities,

Proposition 3.
$$Va_{win H} - Va_{loss H} > Va_{win L} - Va_{loss L} .$$

Proposition 3 states that high- and low-status opponents have unequal effects upon the algebraic differences between the valences of wins and losses. The derivation that follows shows how tension should theoretically vary with these differences between valences.

a. By substituting probability and valence for force in accordance with Assumptions A and B, we obtain the following transformation of Assumption C:

$$t = F(\text{Pr}_G \times \text{Va}_G + \text{Pr}_A \times \text{Va}_A) .$$

b. In the present competitive situation, wins and losses are mutually exclusive; a change in the probability of attaining the goal, ΔPr_G, implies an opposite change in the probability of occurrence of the avoidance, ΔPr_A. From the preceding proposition, the change in tension level, Δt, with these changes in probability is

$$\Delta t = F(\Delta\text{Pr}_G \times \text{Va}_G - \Delta\text{Pr}_A \times \text{Va}_A) .$$

c. Since wins and losses are mutually exclusive, the changes in their probabilities are not only opposite in direction but equal in magnitude, $|\Delta\text{Pr}_G| = |\Delta\text{Pr}_A|$. By substitution, we obtain

$$\Delta t = F(\Delta\text{Pr}_G \times \text{Va}_G - \Delta\text{Pr}_G \times \text{Va}_A) .$$

d. This proposition simplifies to Proposition 4.

Proposition 4.

$$\Delta t = F[\Delta\text{Pr}_G(\text{Va}_G - \text{Va}_A)] .$$

Proposition 4 states that shifts in tension will vary with shifts in the probability of a goal, depending on the algebraic difference between positive and negative valences.

The terms of Proposition 4 can be readily applied to the present experiment. Subjects know immediately upon completing a trial whether they have won or lost. The probability of winning a trial rises by unity from a known loss ($\text{Pr}_{\text{win}} = 0$) to a known win ($\text{Pr}_{\text{win}} = 1$); this rise in the probability of winning implies that ΔPr_G is equal to 1 in Proposition 4. The difference in tension levels between a win and a loss, $t_{\text{win}} - t_{\text{loss}}$, can be substituted for Δt in Proposition 4. As applied to the present circumstances, Proposition 4 then states that the algebraic difference in tension between a win and a loss varies directly with the algebraic difference in valence between a win and a loss:

Proposition 4A.

$$t_{\text{win}} - t_{\text{loss}} = F(\text{Va}_{\text{win}} - \text{Va}_{\text{loss}}) .$$

We have seen in Proposition 3 that the algebraic difference in valence between a win and a loss is greater against a high-status opponent than against a low-status one. It follows from Proposition 4A that:

HYPOTHESIS 1.

$$t_{\text{win H}} - t_{\text{loss H}} > t_{\text{win L}} - t_{\text{loss L}} .$$

Hypothesis 1, which is tested below, predicts an interaction effect of given direction. It states that the algebraic difference in tension between a win and a loss is greater when the subject competes against a high-status opponent than it is when he competes against a low-status one.

Procedure

Each of 32 male undergraduates at New York University performed 14 mirror-tracing tasks. Subjects were able to see only the mirror images of different drawings while attempting to trace the outlines. The experimenter presented the experiment as a test of poise and self-assurance in a competition designed to assess the subject as well as New York University students in general. To half the subjects, the experimenter introduced their opponent—actually the experimenter's confederate—as one of a group of local factory workers (low status). To the other half, he introduced the opponent as a scion of a socially prominent family from an Ivy League college (high status).

The two competitors, each accompanied by an experimenter, worked in adjoining rooms connected by a one-way screen. The flip of a two-headed coin resulted in the subject's opponent's always going first in tracing each figure. The experimenter in the adjoining room, observing the subject through the one-way screen, gave him fictitious feedback during each trial on how his tracing compared with that of his opponent.

Every figure was divided into seven segments. As the subject completed each segment, the experimenter either sounded a buzzer to indicate that the subject did worse than his opponent or refrained from sounding the buzzer to indicate that the subject did better. Three or fewer buzzes over the seven segments signified a win; four or more buzzes signified a loss. Following a prearranged schedule, the experimenter signaled the subject that he won half the tasks and lost half.

The schedule of buzzes also conveyed information about the probability of winning or losing a given trial. On each task, subjects paused briefly after the fourth segment (4/7-point). The schedule of buzzes up to this stopping point was as follows. Four tasks received only one buzz up to the 4/7-point; the probability of winning such a trial was relatively high, and subjects always ended by winning that trial. Four other tasks received three buzzes by the 4/7-point; the probability of winning was relatively low, and subjects always ended by losing the trial. The remaining six tasks received two buzzes by the 4/7-point; the probability of winning was intermediate, and subjects ended by winning half and losing half of these trials.*

In summary, as subjects proceeded through the competition, they found themselves in a see-saw battle. During the series of tasks, they were as often behind as ahead of their opponents, and the competition ended in a tie. During single tasks, they were tied at the 4/7-point on six tasks, ahead on four, and behind on four. As a consequence of this stream of information indicating that their ability equaled that of their opponents, subjects came to estimate the probability of over-all success or failure as about equal, whether their opponent was high or low in status.†

At the beginning of the experiment, the experimenter attached bipolar surface electrodes over the extensor muscles of each subject's active forearm (Davis, 1953). He explained that patterns of muscular activity would provide additional measures of poise and self-assurance. To obtain tensional measures while the arm was at rest, the experimenter instructed the subject to pause at the 4/7-point (marked P) and at the 7/7-point (end) of each figure, keeping pen on paper at these pause points until told to remove it. An electroencephalograph amplified and recorded the electromyographic potentials. Following Smith (1953), we measured the largest spike deflection in each .2-second interval during the first two seconds of each pause period. Converted into microvolts, the average of these ten readings constitutes the index of post-movement tension during the pauses on each task.

* There is evidence, given in a fuller report of this study (in preparation), that subjects perceived these six trials as marginal wins and losses in contrast to the clear wins and losses on the remaining eight trials. Since marginal wins and losses are less positively or negatively valent than clear wins and losses, the two types of trials require separate analyses. For brevity, the present report confines itself to the data for the eight clear wins and losses alone, but the data for the marginal wins and losses are consistent with the findings reported below.

† Data, to be presented in the fuller report, show that subjects initially estimated the probability of over-all success as higher against the low-status than against the high-status opponent, but that subsequently they estimated the probability of success as equal (and around .5) for either type of opponent.

Results

Hypothesis 1 states that the algebraic difference between tension levels of wins and losses is greater when the subject competes against a high-status opponent than when he competes against a low-status one. To test Hypothesis 1, we computed each person's mean 7/7-point tension for wins and losses. Table 1 shows the means of these individual means in the high- and low-status treatments.

TABLE 1

*Mean Levels of Muscle Tension for Wins and Losses in
High- and Low-Status Treatments*

| | Task outcome | | |
Status of opponent	Win	Loss	(Win — Loss)
High (n = 16)	171.72	142.31	(+29.41)
Low (n = 16)	154.10	158.81	(−4.71)

| *Analysis of Variance* | | | |
Source	d.f.	M.S.	F
Between high-low	1	5.03	0.0006
Error between subjects	30	8953.85	
Between win-loss	1	2443.08	5.22*
Interaction	1	4656.01	9.95†
Error within subjects	30	468.10	

* $p < .05$.
† $p < .005$.

The predicted interaction is clearly evident in Table 1. Between high- and low-status treatments, there is a significant difference ($p < .005$) between the differences in tension of wins and losses, even without taking direction into account. The predicted direction of the interaction is also evident in the table: the algebraic difference in tension between wins and losses in the high-status treatment (+29.41) exceeds the difference in the low-status treatment (−4.71). The data strongly support Hypothesis 1.

Hypothesis 1 made no assumption about the relationship between positive and negative valences within a treatment. But the differences in tension level that appear in Table 1 imply what this relationship must be. Inspection of Proposition 4A, above, will show that if tension rises from a loss to a win, the difference between the valences of the win and loss must be positive; if tension is constant, the difference must be zero; if tension falls, the difference must be negative. Thus the rise in tension (+29.41) obtained in the high-status condition, implies that the positive valence of winning against the high-status opponent exceeded the negative valence of losing to him; the relatively constant level of tension (−4.91) obtained in the low-status condition implies that the valences of winning and of losing against the low-status opponent were approximately equal.

These implications from the tensional changes *between* wins and losses can be independently checked by tensional changes *within* single wins and single losses. Within a trial that subjects won, the schedule of buzzes in the present experiment informed subjects that the probability of winning was high at the 4/7-point and even higher at the 7/7-point. Within a trial that subjects lost, the buzzes informed subjects that the probability of winning was low at the 4/7-point and even lower at the 7/7-point. The theoretical effects of these shifts in probability upon shifts in tension within a trial can be seen by again considering Proposition 4:

$$\Delta t = F\left[\Delta Pr_{win} \left(Va_{win} - Va_{loss}\right)\right].$$

If the valence of a win exceeds that of a loss in the high-status treatment, the rise in probability of winning from the 4/7- to the 7/7-point of a win should produce a rise in tension between these points ($\Delta t_{win\,H}$ > 0), and the fall in probability of winning from the 4/7- to the 7/7-point of a loss should produce a fall in tension ($\Delta t_{loss\,H}$ < 0). If the valence of a win equals that of a loss in the low-status treatment, neither positive nor negative shifts in probability should affect tension ($\Delta t_{win\,L}$ = 0; $\Delta t_{loss\,L}$ = 0). Expressed in summary form, we have:

HYPOTHESIS 2.

$$\Delta t_{win\,H} - \Delta t_{loss\,H} > \Delta t_{win\,L} - \Delta t_{loss\,L}.$$

Hypothesis 2 states the following interaction: the algebraic difference between shifts in tension of wins and losses should be greater in the high-status than in the low-status treatments. To test the hypothesis, we subtract 4/7-point tension from 7/7-point tension ($t_{7/7} - t_{4/7}$) on each task and compute the algebraic means of these tensional shifts for each subject's respective wins and losses. Table 2 presents the means of these individual means, classified by treatment.

As shown in Table 2, the interaction effect predicted by Hypothesis 2 is significant ($p < .05$), without regard to direction. The direction of the interaction is also consistent with the hypothesis, since the algebraic difference between tensional shifts of passes and fails (+26.80) in the high-status treatment exceeds the algebraic difference (−13.88) in the low-status treatment. Additionally, in accordance with theoretical expectation, tension tends to rise for wins and to fall for losses within the respective cells of the high-status treatment, while the changes within the cells of the low-status treatment more likely lie within the range of random variations around zero. The shifts in tension shown in Table 2 were produced by very small shifts in probability within a trial, from near-certainty about the outcome at the 4/7-point to certainty at the 7/7-point. Level of tension must thus be highly responsive to fluctuations in probability to produce the present confirmation of Hypothesis 2.

TABLE 2

Mean Shifts in Muscle Tension for Wins and Losses in High- and Low-Status Treatments

Status of opponent	Task outcome		(Win − Loss)
	Win	Loss	
High ($n = 16$)	+9.21*	−17.59	(+26.80)
Low ($n = 16$)	−6.33	+7.55	(−13.88)

* A positive score signifies a rise in tension from the 4/7- to the 7/7-point, a negative score the reverse.

Analysis of Variance

Source	d.f.	M.S.	F
Between high-low	1	369.02	0.145
Error between subjects	30	2552.03	
Between win-loss	1	667.31	0.55
Interaction	1	6614.55	5.42*
Error within subjects	30	1220.29	

* $p < .05$.

We may summarize the results of Experiment I by reviewing the logical structure underlying Hypotheses 1 and 2. Both depend on Proposition 4, which expresses how differences in tension (Δt) vary as a function of differences in the probability of winning (ΔPr_{win}) and of differences between positive and negative valences ($Va_{win} - Va_{loss}$). To test Hypothesis 1, we held constant the differences in probability of winning and found that differences in tension varied with differences in valence between wins and losses in the low- and high-status treatments. To test Hypothesis 2, we held constant the differences between positive and negative valences and found that differences in tension varied with differences in probability of winning between the earlier and later points of a task. Hence, in confirming Hypotheses 1 and 2, we obtain support for the assumptions underlying Proposition 4 regarding the dependence of tension upon both probability and valence.

Discussion

The complexity of the derivations given above arises from the lack of a direct measure of the relationship between the positive and negative valences of a task. If we had known this relationship, we could have stated how wins and losses affect tension levels rather than differences between tension levels. But to determine the relative strengths of positive and negative valences ordinarily requires a separate and laborious parametric study. The experiment reported here thus illustrates the difficulty raised for psychological research by the lack of a direct, behavioral measure of the relationship between the positive and negative valences of single tasks.

The test of Hypothesis 2, above, indicates a method for establishing the relative strengths of these valences. As the likelihood of winning becomes either more or less certain from the middle to the end of a trial, tension rises if the valence of winning is greater than that of losing, but falls if the reverse is true. By observing fluctuations in tension during a trial whose outcome is known, one can ascertain whether the aversiveness of failure is greater than or less than the attractiveness of success. Conversely, as shown in Experiment III, below, by observing fluctuations in tension during a trial in which the relationship between valences is known, one can ascertain whether subjects experienced a given outcome as a success or as a failure.

Apart from measurement implications, our findings bear on the wider issue of muscular tension as act or activation. The findings are clearly incompatible with the assumption that level of activation rises with drive arousal or punishment and falls with drive reduction or reward (Malmo, 1959), since tension was highest with the most rewarding outcome (a win against a high-status opponent), but only intermediate with the most punishing outcome (a loss against a low-status opponent). The results are also incompatible with the assumption that level of activation rises with uncertainty and falls with certainty (Berlyne, 1960). Certainty about winning against a high-status opponent produced higher tension than uncertainty, while certainty and uncertainty about either winning or losing produced equal tension against a low-status opponent. These findings are difficult to reconcile with the view that links muscular tension to physiological activation, but they follow predictably from the view that tension varies with probability and valence as do other psychological acts.

Experiment II. *Tension as a Function of the Probability of Success or Failure in Tests with High or Low Passing Scores*

The preceding experiment manipulated the valences of over-all success and failure; the next experiment manipulates their probabilities. In a series of trials, the passing score is usually expressed as some proportion of test items that must be passed. The lower this passing score, e.g., 25% rather than 75%, the *more* any single pass increases the probability of over-all success and the *less* any single fail increases the probability of over-all failure. Using a high passing score in one treatment (high passing score) and a low passing score in the other (low passing score), we vary the probabilities of over-all success and failure while holding constant the number of trials that subjects pass or fail.

Since a single pass contributes more to over-all success with a low than with a high passing score, the positive valence of a single pass in the low condition (Va_{passL}) should be greater than that in the high condition (Va_{passH}). Since a single fail contributes less to over-all failure with a low than with a high passing score, the negative valence of a single fail in the low condition (Va_{failL}) should be less than that in the high condition (Va_{failH}). These relationships among the valences of single trials can be expressed as follows:

Proposition 5.

$$Va_{pass\,L} > Va_{pass\,H} \; ,$$

Proposition 6.

$$Va_{fail\,L} < Va_{fail\,H} \; ,$$

and, by subtraction,

Proposition 7.

$$Va_{pass\,L} - Va_{fail\,L} > Va_{pass\,H} - Va_{fail\,H} \; .$$

The foregoing inequalities among valences are formally similar to those of Experiment I. They lead, by the same line of derivation used in Experiment I, to the following relationship among levels of tension:

HYPOTHESIS 3.

$$t_{pass\,L} - t_{fail\,L} > t_{pass\,H} - t_{fail\,H} \; .$$

Hypothesis 3, like its counterpart, Hypothesis 1, predicts an interaction effect with a given direction: the algebraic difference in tension between single passes and fails is greater when the passing score of a test is low than when it is high. This hypothesis is tested in the experiment described below.

Procedure

Each of 30 subjects, male undergraduates at New York University, performed 12 of the 14 mirror-tracing tasks used in Experiment I. The experimenter described the tasks as part of a non-verbal test of "practical intelligence" which could effectively predict subjects' future occupational success. The experimenter told half the subjects that, in order to achieve the standard of an average college student, they needed to pass three of the twelve tasks (low passing score), and told the other half that they needed to pass six of the twelve tasks (high passing score). Referring to a fictitious chart, the experimenter assured subjects that below-average performance destined them for menial jobs, but that above-average performance destined them for prestigeful positions in later life.

On attaching the electrodes to subjects' forearms, the experimenter explained that the test was machine-scored according to a complex formula which took account of rate of improvement in accuracy, speed, and muscular coordination relative to the degree of difficulty

of each task. This deliberately ambiguous statement aimed to fore-
stall suspicion about the standardized announcements of passes and
fails that the experimenter would subsequently use. As in the previous experiment, subjects paused briefly at two points, after completing approximately three quarters of a tracing (3/4-point) and after
reaching the end (4/4-point). During the interval in which the machine allegedly scored a trial, the experimenter requested subjects to
state whether they had judged their work as passing or as failing at
the 3/4-point and the 4/4-point, respectively. After obtaining the subjects' statements, the experimenter announced the machine score at
the 4/4-point. The announcements followed a pre-arranged schedule,
which resulted in the subjects' passing or failing half the tasks.

The present experiment, unlike the previous one, does not permit
us to classify tasks as passes or fails by the experimenter's announcements. The announcements kept subjects from judging the tasks as
either all passes or all fails. But whether the experimenter announced
a pass or a fail *after* a particular trial had no effect on whether subjects experienced a pass or fail *during* that trial. In order to relate the
tension level of a task to the contemporaneous experience of passing
or failing it, we must therefore rely on subjects' reports of their subjective experience.

There is evidence, however, that when subjects reported their 4/4-
point judgment, they were influenced by what they anticipated the
experimenter would shortly announce. On approximately 30 per cent
of the tasks, subjects reported that their judgments at the 4/4-point
differed from those at the 3/4-point. These shifts were predominantly
from pass to fail in the low passing score treatment, in which the passing score of 25% must have suggested that the experimenter would
announce relatively many fails; the shifts were predominantly from
fail to pass in the high passing score treatment, in which the passing
score of 50% must have suggested that the experimenter would announce relatively many passes.* The anticipation of the experimenter's announcements thus exerted greater influence on subjects' 4/4-
point reports than on their 3/4-point reports, perhaps because sub-

---

* In the low passing score treatment, 72 per cent of the shifts were in the pass-to-
fail direction; in the high passing score treatment, 74 per cent were in the fail-to-
pass direction. The distributions of the two types of shifts differ between treatments
beyond the .001 level.

jects believed that the experimenter could check their 4/4-point judgments against the scores of the machine. In any case, subjects' reports appear to reflect their actual experience of passing or failing at the 4/4-point less accurately than at the 3/4-point.

The analysis that follows classifies passes and fails according to subjects' 3/4-point reports, and examines tension at these points as well. To score tension, we employ the procedures described in Experiment I. To compare differences in tension between passes and fails in the low passing score and high passing score treatments, we again employ a repeated-measurements, analysis-of-variance design (Lindquist, 1953).

Results

Hypothesis 3 predicts an interaction effect in which the algebraic difference in tension level between passes and fails is greater in the low than in the high passing score treatment. Table 3 presents the means of each subject's mean 3/4-point tension in tasks judged as 3/4-point passes or fails in the low and high treatments.

TABLE 3

Mean Tension Levels of 3/4-Point Passes and Fails for
Subjects in Low and High Passing Score Treatments

| Passing score | Judged outcome | | (Pass − Fail) |
	Pass	Fail	
Low (n = 15)	158.55	140.91	(+17.64)
High (n = 15)	157.85	172.63	(−14.78)

Analysis of Variance

Source	d.f.	M.S.	F
Between high-low	1	3607.62	0.74
Error between subjects	28	4895.64	
Between pass-fail	1	30.65	0.44
Interaction	1	3943.58	55.95*
Error within subjects	28	70.48	

* $p < .001$.

TABLE 4

*Relative Frequencies with Which Subjects Display Greater or Lesser
3/4-Point Tension for Passes than Fails in Low and High
Passing Score Treatments*

	Tension for passes vs. fails	
Passing score	t pass $>$ t fail	t pass $<$ t fail
Low ($n = 15$)	14	1
High ($n = 15$)	0	15

Exact probability: $p \doteq .000$ (Mainland *et al.*, 1956).

In accordance with Hypothesis 3, the interaction effect is highly significant ($p < .001$), even if the prediction about direction is not taken into account. The directional prediction is confirmed as well. While the algebraic difference in tension between passes and fails is positive ($+17.64$) in the low treatment, it is negative (-14.78) in the high treatment. The data give clear-cut support to Hypothesis 3.

The interaction effect obtained in the present experiment appears to be stronger than that obtained in Experiment I. Indeed, the effect of manipulating passing scores is so great* that there is virtually no overlap in the tensional patterns displayed by subjects in the two treatments. All but one subject in the low treatment showed greater tension for passes than for fails; all subjects in the high treatment showed greater tension for fails than for passes (Table 4).

We showed in Experiment I that one can derive from differences in tension between wins and losses the relative strengths of the posi-

---

* The derivation of Hypothesis 3 assumes that the differences between the probabilities of passing a judged 3/4-pass and of failing a judged 3/4-fail are equal in the two treatments. On this assumption, the experimental manipulations must have produced sizeable inequalities in the differences between the valence of a pass and that of a fail in each treatment. Conceivably, however, the difference between the probabilities of a pass and a fail are greater in the high treatment than the low treatment. Subjects could well view each item in the test as easier to pass with a high than with a low passing score. The probability of passing an item would then be greater in the high treatment than in the low treatment ($Pr_{passH} > Pr_{passL}$) and the probability of failing an item would be less in the high treatment than in the low treatment ($Pr_{failH} < Pr_{failL}$). It follows that ($Pr_{passH} - Pr_{failH}$) $>$ ($Pr_{passL} - Pr_{failL}$). To produce the results of Table 3, the differences between the valences of a pass and those of a fail in the two treatments would have to be even more markedly unequal on this assumption than on the assumption made in the text.

tive and negative valences of wins and losses. In the present experiment, too, if tension for a pass exceeds that for a fail, the valence of a pass must exceed that of a fail; if tension for a pass is less than that for a fail, the valence of a fail must exceed that of a pass. The results of Tables 3 and 4 thus imply that the positive valence of a pass is greater than the negative valence of a fail in the low passing score treatment and that the reverse obtains in the high passing score treatment.

Experiment I also demonstrated how one could predict from differences in tension *between* tasks the shifts in tension *within* tasks. Proposition 4 implies that if the valence of a pass exceeds that of a fail, the change in tension within a task varies directly with the change in probability of *passing* the task. Proposition 4 implies, too, that if the valence of a fail exceeds that of a pass, the change in tension within a task varies directly with the change in probability of *failing* the task.* In general:

Proposition 8. The shift in tension during a task varies directly with the shift in subjective probability of whichever task outcome (pass or fail) has the greater valence.

In what follows, we take subjects' reports of shifts in judgment of passing or failing from the 3/4- to the 4/4-point of a task to indicate shifts in the subjective probability of the outcome. If subjects' 4/4-point reports reflected their anticipation of the experimenter's announcements, these reports need not correspond with subjects' actual judgments of passing or failing. Nevertheless, subjects should be more likely to report a shift from a pass to a fail where they viewed their work as worsening rather than improving between the 3/4- and 4/4-points of a task. Similarly, they should be more likely to report a shift from a fail to a pass where they viewed their work as improving rather than worsening between these points. Thus a reported shift in judgment between the 3/4- and 4/4-points of a task should correspond in some degree to an actually experienced shift in the probability of passing or failing.

According to Proposition 8, the shift in tension during a trial is a

---

* Proposition 4 states that $\Delta t = F\,[\Delta Pr_{pass}\,(Va_{pass} - Va_{fail})]$. Where $Va_{pass} - Va_{fail}$ is positive and held constant, $\Delta t = F\,(\Delta Pr_{pass})$. But in the present situation we have $\Delta Pr_{pass} = -\Delta Pr_{fail}$; hence Proposition 4 can be rewritten as $\Delta t = F\,[\Delta Pr_{fail}\,(Va_{fail} - Va_{pass})]$. Where $(Va_{fail} - Va_{pass})$ is positive and held constant, we have $\Delta t = F\,(\Delta Pr_{fail})$.

direct function of the shift in probability of whichever outcome has the greater valence. For tasks in the low passing score treatment, the valence of passing exceeds that of failing. If a fail-to-pass shift in judgment signifies an increase in the probability of passing, these tasks should exhibit a rise in tension; if a pass-to-fail shift signifies a decrease in the probability of passing, these tasks should exhibit a fall in tension. For tasks in the high passing score treatment, by contrast, the valence of failing exceeds that of passing. If a fail-to-pass shift signifies a decrease in the probability of failing, these tasks should exhibit a fall in tension; if a pass-to-fail shift signifies an increase in the probability of failing, they should exhibit a rise in tension. In summary:

HYPOTHESIS 4. In the low passing score treatment, fail-to-pass tasks rise in tension with greater relative frequency than pass-to-fail tasks; in the high passing score treatment, pass-to-fail tasks rise in tension with greater relative frequency than fail-to-pass tasks.

Table 5 compares the relative frequencies with which each type of task rises or falls in 3/4-point to 4/4-point tension in the two treatments.

The interaction effect predicted by Hypothesis 4 clearly appears in Table 5. In the low treatment, relatively more fail-to-pass tasks (54 per cent) rise in tension than pass-to-fail tasks (35 per cent); in the high treatment, relatively more pass-to-fail tasks (73 per cent) rise in tension than fail-to-pass tasks (33 per cent). A one-tailed chi-

TABLE 5

*Relative Frequencies with Which Tasks Rise or Fall in 3/4- to
4/4-Point Tension as a Function of Shifts in Pass-Fail
Judgments in Two Treatments*

	Treatment			
	Low passing score		High passing score	
	A	B	C	D
Shift in judgment	Pass-to-Fail	Fail-to-Pass	Pass-to-Fail	Fail-to-Pass
Rise in tension	12 (35%)	7 (54%)	11 (73%)	14 (33%)
Fall in tension	22	6	4	28
Total	34	13	15	42

Over-all, $x^2 = 6.639$, 3 d.f., $p < .05$, one tail.
Interaction: $(A + D)$ vs. $(B + C)$, $x^2 = 6.400$, 1 d.f., $p < .01$, one tail; A vs. B, $x^2 = .684$, 1 d.f., n.s.; C vs. D, $x^2 = 5.649$, 1 d.f., $p < .01$, one tail.

square test underestimates the significance level of the direction and magnitude of the interaction but is nonetheless significant beyond the .05 level ($\chi^2 = 6.639$, 3 d.f., $p < .05$, one tail). Despite the insensitivity of analyzing frequency data alone, the present results parallel those obtained by the analysis-of-variance test used in Experiment I (Table 2), which examined the amount as well as the direction of tensional shifts within tasks.*

In Experiment I, the tensional changes within a task—corresponding to shifts from near-certainty to certainty about the outcome—reflected very small changes in probability. In the present experiment, the tensional changes—corresponding to subjects' reversing their reports of passing or failing between two points of a task—evidently reflect greater changes in probability. In any case, the evidence of both experiments clearly shows the dependence of tension upon fluctuations in probability.

Discussion

The direct effect of manipulating passing scores in the present experiment was to vary the probability of over-all success or failure. The direct effect of manipulating status of opponent in Experiment I was to vary the valence of over-all success and failure. Both types of experimental manipulations converge in their effects upon the valences of single tasks in the series. Given this convergence, the theoretical analyses of both experiments could proceed in parallel.

Hypothesis 1 in Experiment I and Hypothesis 3 in the present experiment are formally identical. Each expresses the effect of differences between the strength of positive and negative valences upon differences in tension between positive and negative outcomes. Hypothesis 2 in Experiment I and Hypothesis 4 in the present experiment are similarly related. Each expresses the effect of differences between the probabilities of an outcome upon differences in tension between earlier and later points of a task. The confirmatory results of one experiment reinforce those of the other in support of each type of hypothesis.

* The mean amounts and directions of 3/4- to 4/4-point tensional shifts for tasks in Table 5 are as follows: Low passing score, fail-to-pass tasks (+12.43), pass-to-fail tasks (−11.03); high passing score, fail-to-pass tasks (−7.15), pass-to-fail tasks (+31.16).

The present experiment adds a new bit of information about the impact of a shift in probability upon the shift in tension during a task. In Experiment I, the positive valence exceeded the negative valence in one treatment, while the two valences were approximately equal in the other treatment. In Experiment II, the positive valence again exceeded the negative valence in one treatment, but the negative valence exceeded the positive valence in the other. Both experiments show that if the positive valence exceeds the negative one, tension rises with an increase in the probability of the positive outcome. Experiment II shows, in addition, that where the negative valence exceeds the positive one, tension rises with an increase in the probability of the negative outcome. This finding reinforces the point noted above that shifts in tension during a task can be used to measure the relative strengths of the positive and negative valences of the task.

Finally, Experiment II re-emphasizes the difficulties inherent in the view that tension is an index of level of activation. Level of activation refers to a relatively stable state of physiological arousal, exemplified by sleep or wakefulness, that operates as a background for psychological functioning. But both experiments show that moment-to-moment shifts in probability and valence produce immediate shifts in tension. These specific, transitory effects seem hardly compatible with the view that a change in tension represents a change in the general state of the organism. They are clearly compatible, however, with the view that a change in tension is a specific psychological act.

Experiment III. *Muscular Tension and Task Recall*

The history of work on the Zeigarnik effect (Zeigarnik, 1927) has been plagued by a kind of circularity. In the light of researches following that of Zeigarnik, it appears that task-oriented subjects recall more psychologically interrupted tasks than psychologically completed ones (Marrow, 1938; Lewis and Franklin, 1944). But it also appears that ego-oriented subjects, when they interpret interruptions as failures and completions as successes, recall more completed tasks than interrupted ones (Rosenzweig, 1943; Lewis and Franklin, 1944). Given these opposing tendencies, it is difficult to disconfirm Zeigarnik's hypothesis. Where subjects fail to exhibit the effect, the possibility exists that they have become ego-involved despite the experimenter's task-oriented instructions. The possibility also exists that they have interpreted objectively interrupted tasks as finished and objectively completed tasks as unfinished despite the experimenter's manipulations. We lack precise means for determining the psychological states of subjects during task performance. If we have sufficient confidence in the existence of the effect, we can only assume but cannot demonstrate that negative instances have failed to meet the conditions for an adequate test.

The present experiment illustrates the problem once again and indicates how tensional measures may aid in its solution. The experiment was undertaken to resolve an issue raised by Forrest (1959) regarding a finding reported by Smith (1953). Smith found that, under task-oriented conditions, post-movement muscular tension was greater for interrupted tasks than for completed ones. Forrest extended this study by manipulating task- and ego-orientations—apparently successfully, since recall of unfinished tasks was high under his task-oriented instructions while recall of finished tasks was high under his ego-oriented instructions. He found that post-movement tension was greater for unfinished than for finished tasks in both treatments. The result was inconsistent with a neurological theory proposed by Smith, and led Forrest to question whether the tensional effect was not a motor artifact, "due to the sudden prevention of the continuance of a skilled movement" (p. 184).*

The issue raised by Forrest is no longer germane. In the two studies reported above, all tasks were objectively finished, yet tensional effects appeared without sudden discontinuance of movement. However, prior to these studies, Forrest's query led us to design an experiment in which subjects, given task-oriented instructions on a set of mirror-tracing tasks, either halted work at the 3/4-point of a tracing or paused at this point before proceeding to the 4/4-point. The experiment is of interest only because the manipulations did not appear to produce their intended effects. Despite the task-oriented instructions, subjects recalled a somewhat larger number of completed tasks than interrupted ones, which suggests that at least some subjects may

* With hindsight, we may ask whether Forrest was not throwing Smith's fact away with his theory. We have seen, above, that tension for failures may be greater or less than tension for successes, depending on the respective valences and probabilities of failure and success. Forrest's results suggest that his ego-oriented subjects regarded either the valence or the probability of over-all failure as greater than those of over-all success.

have become ego-involved.* Further confounding matters, subjects
appeared to regard many of the objectively interrupted tasks as finished—perhaps because the experimenter gave them advance notice
of his interruptions. They also appeared to regard many of the objectively completed tasks as unfinished—perhaps because of the difficulty of doing satisfactory mirror-tracings of the figures.† It thus
seemed possible that tasks subject to identical manipulations were
variously experienced by subjects as successes, failures, interruptions, or completions.

Given this possible conglomerate of types of tasks, we set the problem that is pursued below: can tensional measures distinguish each
of the four classes of tasks and thereby predict their differential recall? In dealing with this problem, we show first how approach or
avoidance forces should theoretically operate for each type of task
and, second, how these forces should manifest themselves in muscular tension during performance.

Distinguishing task-oriented from ego-oriented performance. Task-
oriented instructions typically deny the possibility that working
on a task can lead to success or failure. They rely on the subject's
becoming sufficiently interested in the problem per se that he will
set the goal of completing the task as an "end in itself." By contrast,
ego-oriented instructions emphasize that the task can lead to success
or failure. While a task-oriented subject is acted on by approach
forces alone, an ego-oriented subject is acted on by both approach
and avoidance forces. In general, the sum of the magnitudes of two
forces should be greater than the magnitude of a single force. By
Assumption C, tasks performed under ego-oriented conditions should
thus exhibit a higher level of tension than tasks performed under
task-oriented conditions. Using level of tension during a task to distinguish task- from ego-oriented performance, we have:

Proposition 9. The relative frequency of ego-oriented tasks should
be greater among high-tension than among low-tension tasks; the relative frequency of task-oriented tasks should be greater among low-
tension than among high-tension tasks.

* Subjects recalled 47 per cent of the completed tasks and 40 per cent of the interrupted ones; the difference is not significant.
† In a recognition test administered approximately five minutes after the experiment,
subjects identified only 53 per cent of the interrupted tasks as unfinished and only
62 per cent of the completed tasks as finished.

Proposition 9 implies that by sorting tasks in terms of level of tension we can separate interruptions and completions from successes and failures. For *task-oriented* interruptions and completions should exhibit relatively low tension, while *ego-oriented* successes and failures should exhibit relatively high tension. We show next that by a second sorting, in terms of shift in tension, we can separate interruptions from completions and successes from failures. Each of the four types of tasks should then be distinguishable by the double classification of level of tension and shift in tension.

Distinguishing task-oriented interruptions from task oriented completions. This analysis applies to tasks which subjects have traced to the 4/4-point and which therefore provide data on 3/4- to 4/4-point tensional shifts. If such tasks are psychologically completed, the force at the 3/4-point to approach the goal should decrease to zero at the 4/4-point. If the tasks are psychologically interrupted, the force at the 3/4-point to approach the goal should continue to operate at the 4/4-point. Indeed, if the subject perceives that the probability of goal-attainment has increased between the 3/4- and the 4/4-point, the force toward the goal should increase between these points (Assumption A).* By Assumption C, a shift in force should produce a corresponding shift in tension. Thus psychological completions should decrease in tension between the 3/4- and the 4/4-point, but only psychological interruptions should increase in tension. Since task-oriented completions and interruptions should exhibit in addition a relatively low level of tension (Proposition 9), it follows that

Proposition 10. For low-tension tasks the relative frequency of psychological completions is greater among tasks that fall than among those that rise in tension; the relative frequency of psychological interruptions is greater among tasks that rise than among those that fall in tension.

Distinguishing ego-oriented successes from ego-oriented failures. For ego-oriented tasks, the shift in tension with success or failure depends on the relative strengths of the valences of success and failure (Experiments I and II, above). In the present experiment, the task-oriented instructions strongly emphasized that subjects would not

---

* The subject may also perceive that the probability of goal-attainment has decreased between the 3/4- and the 4/4-point. In this case, the force toward the goal should also decrease, even though the task is psychologically interrupted.

and could not be evaluated by their work on the tasks. We make the intuitive assumption that subjects who nevertheless became ego-oriented were high in fear of failure (Atkinson, 1953); i.e., they viewed the aversiveness of failure as greater than the attractiveness of success.* As in Experiment I, subjects should generally be more certain about whether they have passed or failed an item at the 4/4-point of a trial than at the 3/4-point. If the valence of failure exceeds that of success, then according to Proposition 8 tension should rise as subjects become more certain of failure and should fall as they become more certain of success. We may thus distinguish tasks experienced as successes or failures as follows:

Proposition 11. For high-tension tasks the relative frequency of psychological successes is greater among tasks that fall than among those that rise in tension; the relative frequency of psychological failures is greater among tasks that rise than among those that fall in tension.

The foregoing propositions give tensional criteria for distinguishing the four types of tasks that should differentially affect recall. According to Proposition 10, low-tension tasks that fall in tension should indicate psychological completions, while those that rise in tension should indicate psychological interruptions. According to Proposition 11, high-tension tasks that fall in tension should indicate psychological successes, while those that rise in tension should indicate psychological failures. To validate these propositions, we inquire below whether they in fact predict differential recall. Since interruptions should be better recalled than completions, and successes should be better recalled than failures, it follows that

HYPOTHESIS 5. For low-tension tasks, recall is greater for tasks that rise than for those that fall in tension; for high-tension tasks, recall is greater for tasks that fall than for those that rise in tension.

---

* The grounds for this assumption are as follows: If subjects doubted our statements that they were not being tested, they probably regarded the statements as false reassurances. To give false reassurances about a test implies a desire to conceal its potentially unpleasant outcomes. Moreover, the mere fact of being psychologically tested is frequently aversive. This stems, we suggest, from subjects' feelings (a) that the negative findings of a psychological examination are more threatening than the positive findings are gratifying, (b) that subjects' personal characteristics or our own as psychologists make it more likely than not that we will find them wanting.

Hypothesis 5 is tested by means of data obtained from the experiment described below.

Procedure

Subjects were 17 female undergraduates at New York University, each of whom performed 12 mirror tracings of different outlines of simple objects. Subjects were instructed to pause briefly at a point approximately three-quarters through the tracing (3/4-point), and at the end (4/4-point). During these rest intervals, electromyographic measures were taken of the forearm extensors of subjects' writing arms.

Instructions were adapted from those used for Forrest's (1959) task-oriented treatment. The experimenter informed subjects that the purpose of the study was not to investigate their ability, but to pretest the figures for later research on muscular activity during drawing. Six tasks were objectively completed and six were objectively interrupted at the 3/4-point. In explanation of the interruptions, the experimenter stated that, to save time, the tracings would be discontinued whenever she obtained enough information about the figures from partial performance. For interrupted tasks, the experimenter announced midway through the tasks that subjects should halt work after the 3/4-point; for completed tasks, the experimenter made no such announcement.

Approximately three minutes after completion of the series of tasks, the experimenter announced that she wished to get subjects' reactions to the pictures. She requested subjects to "write down the names of any of the pictures that you can recall . . . any that come to your mind." One and a half minutes were allowed for recall, after which the experimenter presented to the subjects a sheet containing small scale drawings of the figures and asked them to identify those which they had or had not finished.

The data thus available are frequency of recall, frequency of identification of tasks as finished or unfinished, tension level after the 3/4-point, and, for objectively completed tasks, tension level after the 4/4-point. In testing Hypothesis 5, which requires information about 3/4- to 4/4-point shifts in tension, we consider only that half of the tasks which subjects objectively completed. Because of machine failures, the electromyographic recordings of ten of these tasks were unscorable, leaving 92 available for analysis.

Results

Hypothesis 5 asserts that low-tension tasks elicit superior recall when they rise in tension but that high-tension tasks elicit superior recall when they fall in tension. To classify tasks as high or low in tension, we take as an arbitrarily selected cutoff the mean 3/4-point tension of all tasks ($\bar{t}_{3/4} = 136.8$ microvolts). A task is classified as high or low in tension, respectively, if its own 3/4-point tension is above or below this mean. To classify tasks as rising or falling in tension, we compare differences in tension at their 3/4- and 4/4 points. On several tasks, tension was equal at these points; on several others, the differences were small enough to have been produced by errors in our hand measurement of peaks in the recordings. As an arbitrarily selected criterion for eliminating such tasks from the analysis, we take the quartile division comprising those tasks which shifted least between their 3/4- and 4/4-points, namely, tasks for which $t_{3/4} = t_{4/4}$ $\pm$ 12 microvolts.* A task is thus classified as rising in tension if it increases by more than 12 microvolts from the 3/4- to the 4/4-point (i.e., if $t_{4/4} > t_{3/4} + 12$) and as falling in tension, if it decreases by more than 12 microvolts between these points (i.e., if $t_{4/4} < t_{3/4} -$ 12). Table 6 shows the relative frequencies with which subjects recalled tasks grouped according to tension level and tensional shift.

TABLE 6

Relative Frequencies with Which Tasks are Recalled as a Function of Level of Tension and 3/4- to 4/4-Point Tensional Shifts

	Tension level of tasks			
	Low		High	
3/4-to 4/4-point tensional shift	A Rise	B Fall	C Rise	D Fall
Recalled	12 (57%)	4 (20%)	2 (25%)	13 (65%)
Not recalled	9	16	6	7
Total	21	20	8	20

Over-all, $x^2 = 10.83$, 3 d.f., $p < .01$, one tail.
Interaction: (A + D) vs. (B + C), $x^2 = 8.99$, 1 d.f., $p < .005$, one tail; A vs. B, $x^2 = 4.63$, 1 d.f., $p < .025$, one tail; C vs. D, exact $p = .066$, one tail.

* This procedure eliminated 23 of the 92 objectively completed tasks that were available for analysis.

The data of Table 6 show a clear-cut interaction effect as predicted by Hypothesis 5. Among low-tension tasks, recall is *greater* for those tasks that rise (57 per cent) rather than fall in tension (20 per cent); but among high-tension tasks, recall is *less* for tasks that rise (25 per cent) rather than fall in tension (65 per cent). By a one-tailed χ^2 test, which underestimates the significance level of the direction and magnitude of the interaction, the over-all differences are still significant beyond the .01 level. The pattern of differential recall among these tasks conforms to what would be expected if low-tension tasks that rise or fall in tension correspond respectively to psycho logical interruptions or completions and if high-tension tasks that rise or fall in tension correspond respectively to psychological failures or successes. The data on recall thus validate the present use of tensional measures for analyzing subjects' psychological states during task performance.

Subjects' psychological states during performance should be represented in their phenomenal experience as well as in their muscles. The question naturally arises about what degree of correspondence, if any, exists between these two domains of psychological functioning.

After the series of trials, the experimenter presented small scale drawings of the figures to subjects and asked them to identify which they had or had not finished, referring by the question to what tracings the experimenter had or had not allowed them to complete. We noted above the surprising amount of "distortion" in subjects' responses to this problem in recognition, with only 53 per cent of the objective interruptions and 62 per cent of the objective completions being correctly identified by subjects. The result is particularly surprising, since recognition tests are relatively easy and the present one was administered only five minutes after subjects worked on the figures. It seems likely that subjects' identification of the tasks as finished or unfinished reflected their memories not only of the experimenter's treatment of the tasks but of their own psychological states during performance.

We assume that the experience of psychological interruption or failure should produce tendencies to identify a task as unfinished, but that the experience of psychological completion or success should produce tendencies to identify a task as finished. As noted above, these psychological states should also manifest themselves in characteristic shifts in tension: psychological interruption and failure by a rise in tension, psychological completion and success by a fall in tension. We should therefore expect that

HYPOTHESIS 6. For both high- and low-tension tasks, the relative frequency of tasks identified as unfinished is greater among those that rise than among those that fall in tension; the relative frequency of tasks identified as finished is greater among those that fall than among those that rise in tension.

Table 7 shows the relative frequencies with which high- and low-tension tasks were identified as unfinished or finished where they rose or fell in tension from the 3/4- to the 4/4-point.

TABLE 7

Relative Frequencies with Which Tasks are Identified as Finished or Unfinished as a Function of Level of Tension and 3/4- to 4/4-Point Tensional Shifts

	Tension level			
	Low		High	
Tensional shift	A Rise	B Fall	C Rise	D Fall
Identified as unfinished	10 (48%)	3 (15%)	5 (63%)	6 (30%)
Identified as finished	11	17	3	14
Total	21	20	8	20

Over-all, $x^2 = 7.87$, 3 d.f., $p < .025$, one tail.
Interaction: $(A + C)$ vs. $(B + D)$, $x^2 = 5.11$, 1 d.f., $p < .025$, one tail; A vs. B, $x^2 = 3.64$, 1 d.f., $p < .05$, one tail; C vs. D, exact $p = .122$, one tail.

The data of Table 7 confirm Hypothesis 6. With respect to both high- and low-tension tasks, the tendency to identify them as unfinished rather than finished is greater where they rise (48 per cent, 63 per cent) than where they fall (15 per cent, 30 per cent) in tension. The pooled distributions under each type of tensional shift differ beyond the .025 level, taking direction into account. The result is especially noteworthy, since subjects completed the tracings of all tasks represented in Table 7. To identify these objectively completed tasks as unfinished, subjects must have been strongly influenced by having experienced them as interruptions or failures. The confirmation of Hypothesis 6, like that of Hypothesis 5, validates the use of muscular tension in measuring psychological states during task performance.

The confirmation of Hypothesis 6 also indicates that the manifestations of these psychological states are consistent in the subjects' phenomenology and in their muscles.*

Discussion

In Experiment III, we have phenotypically characterized acts as task-oriented or ego-oriented, as interrupted or completed, as successes or failures. But the underlying conception has been that one can capture the essentials of these distinctions by a genotypic analysis of the approach or avoidance tendencies that operate during performance.

We have proposed that muscular deactivation is itself a psychological act and have treated it as included in the larger action of performing a task. The forces that operate in the larger task should operate in muscular deactivation as well. One can therefore measure the forces present in the larger task by measuring the forces present in muscular deactivation. Using muscular tension as an index of the forces present during deactivation, we showed above how tension can be applied to measure the forces that distinguish four types of tasks, each of which differentially affects recall and recognition.

Although the study was directed principally at examining the use of tensional indices in psychological measurement, it also rounds out our examination of Assumption C, regarding the relation of tension to force. Experiments I and II demonstrate that under ego-oriented conditions, tension responds to variations in combined approach–avoidance forces. Experiment III shows that under task-oriented conditions, tension responds to variations in approach forces alone. The study thus adds to the evidence that the same laws that govern molar behavior govern muscular deactivation as well.

Conclusion

We began this chapter by proposing that muscular deactivation, although a small unit of behavior not detectable by the unaided eye,

---

* It should be noted, however, that the phenomenal reports obtained in this experiment are insufficient for predicting differential recall among tasks. Among tasks identified as "finished," the low recall of completions should offset the high recall of successes; among tasks identified as "unfinished" the high recall of interruptions should offset the low recall of failures. Subjects recalled 39 per cent of all tasks they identified as unfinished and 48 per cent of all those they identified as finished, the difference not being significant.

is nevertheless a directed psychological act. We further proposed that level of tension indicates the intensities of the approach–avoidance tendencies that operate during this act. According to these assumptions, muscular deactivation has the same conceptual status as the act of running toward a goal or away from an avoidance; muscular tension has the same status as such other measures of response intensity as speed of running or strength of pull while overcoming a restraint (Miller, 1959). The evidence is clear-cut that in line with these assumptions, muscular deactivation obeys the general psychological laws that relate the strength of approach–avoidance tendencies to the variables of subjective probability and valence.

By contrast to the view proposed here, the construct of level of activation suggests two distinct types of processes for the intensitive and directional components of behavior, intensity being based on physiological functioning, direction being based on psychological functioning. The present findings indicate that, insofar as muscular deactivation is concerned, this dualism not only is unnecessary but directs attention away from the relationship between muscular tension and psychological variables.

One might argue against extending these considerations to a general criticism of the whole of activation theory by noting that muscular relaxation is, after all, a motoric function closely related to directed action. But if muscular tension is discarded as an index of physiological activation, the same may prove necessary for such other indices as heart rate or skin conductance. There is some evidence that these supposedly physiological indicants, too, operate as do other goal-directed behaviors. Bélanger and Feldman (reported in Malmo, 1959) found no heightening of level of activation, as measured by heart rate, among water-deprived rats kept in a restraining compartment; but they did find that heartbeat varied directly with the strength of approach tendencies when these animals were pressing on the lever of a water dispenser in a Skinner box. Epstein and Fenz (1962) found no heightening of level of activation, as measured by galvanic skin response (GSR), among severely conflicted subjects responding to neutral words; they did find that GSR increased with the sum of approach–avoidance tendencies when the subjects were responding to conflict-related words. Neither deprivation nor conflict per se affected heartbeat or GSR, but the strength of approach or avoidance tendencies clearly did. While the authors of both studies state that they are measuring "activation," it seems closer to the fact to state that they are measuring strength of response tendencies.

The construct of level of activation is deeply entrenched in current psychological thinking (Woodworth and Schlosberg, 1954; Duffy, 1957; Malmo, 1959). Woodworth and Schlosberg use the construct, in fact, to organize their discussions of the fields of both motivation and emotion. Whatever the value of the concept of level of activation in physiological research, however, it seems to distract psychological researchers from examining the psychological activities in which their subjects are engaged. Two illustrations follow, drawn from recent investigations of motivation and emotion.

1. Stennett (1957) tested the hypothesis that efficiency of performance varies as an inverted-U-shaped function of level of activation. He employed three treatments which induced successively higher levels of muscular tension and found that performance improved from Treatments I to II but worsened in Treatment III. The apparent support for the hypothesis is vitiated, however, by Stennett's having increased the positive incentives for his subjects from Treatments I to II but having placed them in an approach–avoidance conflict in Treatment III. The decrement in performance in the latter treatment may thus be due not to the physiological effects of high arousal but to the psychological effects of strong conflict.

2. Schachter and Singer (1962) hypothesized that a sympathetically aroused subject who receives an adequate explanation for his bodily sensations will be as impervious as a non-aroused subject to social influences to either euphoria or anger. They found, however, that non-aroused subjects who were injected with a placebo displayed stronger emotional reactions than aroused subjects who were injected with adrenalin and provided with an explanation of their physiological symptoms. Pursuing the possibility that some subjects in the placebo treatment may have become self-aroused, the investigators found that those with higher heart rates showed greater emotionality than those with lower heart rates. This subanalysis is appropriate if variations in heart rate were indicative of physiological activation and were independent of the angry or euphoric reactions. But heightened heart rate is likely to be part of an angry or euphoric response, and the subanalysis may merely show that two measures of the same

response are correlated. The assumption that heart rate is an index of activation may thus have led to confirming a hypothesis by throwing out the disconfirmatory cases.

Viewed in a broader frame, there seems to be an inverse relationship between the size of a unit of behavior and the tendency to treat it as a physiological process. We are accustomed to thinking of bodily changes, if they are sufficiently small, as purely physiological. It seems natural then to undertake a reductive analysis of psychological acts into these physiological elements.

On the other hand, we have no difficulty in treating a molar activity, such as working on an examination, as a psychological act which includes smaller acts, such as working on a test item. Indeed, it is implicit in the conception of goal-directed action that a larger act is the motive of the acts it includes (Chein, 1962). One may inquire, accordingly, how the properties of a larger act influence those of successively smaller ones. The present experiments show that this form of analysis can be extended to quite small acts, of the order of magnitude of a muscle twitch. The experiments thus raise the question whether such an analysis cannot also be made of other supposedly physiological changes. This question reverses the problem of how physiological processes govern molar action; it asks instead how molar action governs molecular acts.

REFERENCES

Atkinson, J. W. The achievement motive and the recall of interrupted and completed tasks. *J. exp. Psychol.*, 1953, **46**, 381–90.

Berlyne, D. E. *Conflict, arousal, and curiosity.* New York: McGraw-Hill, 1960.

Chapman, D., and Volkmann, J. A social determinant of the level of aspiration. *J. abnorm. soc. Psychol.*, 1939, **34**, 225–38.

Chein, I. The image of man. *J. soc. Issues*, 1962, **18**, 1–35.

Davis, J. F. *Manual of surface electromyography.* Montreal: Lab. for Psychol. Stud., McGill Univ., 1953.

Duffy, Elizabeth. The psychological significance of the concept of "arousal" or "activation." *Psychol. Rev.*, 1957, **64**, 265–75.

Edwards, W. Utility, subjective probability, their interaction and variance preferences. *J. conflict Resolut.*, 1962, **6**, 42–51.

English, H. B., and English, Ava C. *A comprehensive dictionary of psychological and psychoanalytical terms.* New York: Longmans, Green, 1958.

Epstein, S., and Fenz, W. Theory and experiment on the measurement of approach–avoidance conflict. *J. abnorm. soc. Psychol.*, 1962, **64**, 97–112.

Forrest, D. W. The role of muscular tension in the recall of interrupted tasks. *J. exp. Psychol.*, 1959, **58**, 181–84.

Lewin, K. The conceptual representation and measurement of psychological forces. *Contr. psychol. Theory*, 1938, **1** (4).

Lewin, K., Dembo, T., Festinger, L., and Sears, Pauline. Level of aspiration. In J. McV. Hunt (Ed.), *Handbook of personality and the behavior disorders*. New York: Ronald, 1944. Pp. 333–78.

Lewis, Helen B., and Franklin, M. An experimental study of the role of the ego in work. *J. exp. Psychol.*, 1944, **34**, 195–215.

Lindquist, E. *Design and analysis of experiments*. Boston: Houghton Mifflin, 1953.

Mainland, D., Herrera, L., and Sutcliffe, M. I. *Tables for use with binomial samples*. New York: Dept. of Medic. Stat., New York Univ., 1956.

Malmo, R. B. Activation: a neuropsychological dimension. *Psychol. Rev.*, 1959, **66**, 367–86.

Marrow, A. J. Goal tensions and recall (I, II). *J. genet. Psychol.*, 1938, **19**, 3–35, 37–64.

Miller, N. E. Liberalization of basic S-R concepts: extensions to conflict behavior, motivation, and social learning. In S. Koch (Ed.), *Psychology, a study of a science*. Vol. 2. New York: McGraw-Hill, 1959. Pp. 196–292.

Rosenzweig, S. An experimental study of repression with special reference to need-persistive and ego-defensive reactions to frustration. *J. exp. Psychol.*, 1943, **32**, 64–74.

Schachter, S., and Singer, I. E. Cognitive, social, and physiological determinants of emotional state. *Psychol. Rev.*, 1962, **69**, 379–99.

Smith, A. A. An electromyographic study of tension in interrupted and completed tasks. *J. exp. Psychol.*, 1953, **46**, 32–36.

Stennett, R. G. The relationship of performance level to level of arousal. *J. exp. Psychol.*, 1957, **54**, 54–61.

Tolman, E. C. Principles of purposive behavior. In S. Koch (Ed.), *Psychology, a study of a science*. Vol. 2. New York: McGraw-Hill, 1959. Pp. 92–157.

Woodworth, R. S., and Schlosberg, H. *Experimental psychology*. New York: Holt, 1954.

Zeigarnik, Bluma. Uber das Behalten erledigter und unerledigter Handlungen. *Psychol. Forsch.*, 1927, **9**, 1–85.

Physiological Covariation
and Sociometric Relationships in Small Peer Groups

HOWARD B. KAPLAN AND NEIL R. BURCH, *Baylor University College of Medicine and Houston State Psychiatric Institute*

SAMUEL W. BLOOM
State University of New York, Downstate Medical Center

A number of investigators—emphasizing, for the most part, a social psychological approach—have studied the meaning of various elements in the social situation *for an individual* as measured by his somatic responsiveness. Only a few reports have considered the *simultaneous* physiological responses of the several participants in social interaction.

Malmo, Boag, and Smith (1957) found that both the subject and the experimenter manifested rapidly falling speech-muscle tension following praise of the patient by the experimenter, and that both displayed non-falling tension following criticism. DiMascio *et al.* (1955) reported a positive correlation between the heart-rate responses of the patient and the therapist for one part of an interview. Coleman, Greenblatt, and Solomon (1956) reported that over a period of 44 interviews the patient's heart rate was highest during periods of anxiety, lowest during depression, and intermediate during hostility. The therapist manifested the *same* pattern of heart-rate response as the patient, except that anxiety was not differentiated from extra-punitive hostility. Finally, DiMascio, Boyd, and Greenblatt (1957) found that both the patient and the therapist manifested higher heart rates during interviews characterized by tension and lower rates during interviews characterized by tension release.

These findings suggest at least two uses for measures of physiological covariation in the study of human social behavior. First, shifts in

This study was supported in part by the National Institute of Mental Health grant M-3360, and in part by Markle Foundation Scholarship.

covariation may serve to identify the content of interaction that has common significance for the participants. Within the course of a single interview the correlation between the physiological responses of the subjects may be positive during one period and negative during another (DiMascio *et al.*, 1955). In the DiMascio, Boyd, and Greenblatt (1957) results noted above, when for 12 interviews *both* the patient and therapist manifested higher heart rates during periods of tension and lower heart rates during periods of tension release, apparently the experiences were of like significance for the participants whether or not the mediating mechanism is interpreted in terms of identification or empathy. However, for antagonistic interaction, the physiological responses were dissimilar. The therapist's heart rate was higher during periods of antagonism while the patient's rate was lower during those same periods. Presumably antagonism was of differential significance to the patient and the therapist, being tension-reducing for the former and tension-inducing for the latter. Thus, on a moment-to-moment basis, the simultaneous variation in physiological response of the participants might provide clues to the specific stimuli (such as verbal content) that have *common* (or dissimilar) tension-inducing or tension-reducing significance.

A second use for measures of physiological covariation is suggested by the findings of Coleman, Greenblatt, and Solomon (1956) cited above. While the patient and the therapist manifested generally similar patterns of physiological response to variations in the patient's affective state, this "physiological relationship" varied somewhat from session to session. The authors concluded from their analysis that the physiological relationship was least likely to be observed when the therapist was disturbed by his own preoccupations or by material relating to his own unresolved conflicts, and was most likely to be manifested when such personal concerns were absent. This conclusion implies that a measure summarizing the physiological relationship (degree of physiological covariation) could serve as an index of the extent to which a broad *range* of stimuli are of common (as opposed to private) significance to the partners in social interaction. A high degree of physiological covariation would presumably indicate a common affective response to the broad and varying stimulus field. A minimum of physiological covariation would reflect idiosyncratic or dissimilar affective responses to the environment. Such a measure would not aim at identifying specific tension-inducing or tension-reducing stimuli as in the first use described above. Rather, by being an index of the common variation in affective significance of a whole range of stimuli, it would be of great value in the investigation of sociological variables that facilitate or impede commonality of affective response in social interaction. For example, changes in the degree of physiological covariation would give an indication of the effects of variations in internal crisis, external threat, power structure, and the communication network on commonality of response.

In this chapter we are concerned with this second use of physiological covariation.

Sociometric Relationship and Physiological Covariation

We shall describe the results of two studies of the effects of variable sociometric relationships—"the web of interpersonal attractions, repulsions, and indifferences that characterize individuals in daily interaction" (Lindzey and Borgatta, 1954, p. 405)—upon physiological covariation.

The sociometric relationship, operationally defined in terms of expressions of liking and disliking, was chosen for the initial application of the concept of physiological covariation. This variable was selected not only because of the important place it occupies in current research on social behavior (Horwitz, 1958; Lindzey and Borgatta, 1954) but also because choices and rejections are in part contingent upon the provision of rewards or the induction of anxiety and discomfort, or both, associated with the persons chosen or rejected (Thibaut and Kelley, 1961). While such factors as reward and anxiety are known to be related to individual physiological response (Lacey, 1959), it is not known whether the same conditions that produce this relationship will also induce physiological covariation.

Physiological covariation is defined in the following studies in terms of the degree of association over time (as indicated by a coefficient of correlation) between the physiological responses of the members of a social relationship. The physiological function chosen for study was the galvanic skin reflex (GSR), generally recognized as a measure that is extremely sensitive to sensory and ideational stimuli (Davis, 1961; Martin, 1961).

The first study was originally reported elsewhere (Kaplan, *et al.*, 1963), but because of its significant relationship to the second study that forms the substance of this chapter, it is herein summarized.

Study 1

The guiding hypothesis of this study was that *when a strong affective orientation (positive or negative) exists between certain members of a group, the affective response of these members to the pattern of interpersonal activity in the group will covary and this covariation of affective response will be reflected in the covariation of their autonomic activity.*

In the evolution of this hypothesis it was reasoned that insofar as the pair members were significant to (affectively oriented toward) each other, the interpersonal activity of these members would also be of common significance, and this common significance would be reflected in common autonomic activity.

Method. A class of sophomore medical students responded to a sociometric questionnaire requesting an indefinite number of names of their classmates that they "like" and "dislike." On the basis of these data, three four-man groups were chosen that may be respectively termed positive, negative, and mixed.

The positive group consisted of four students, each of whom was liked by every other member of the group. The most negative group available consisted of students each of whom was disliked by one other member of the group and none of whom was liked by any other member of the group. The mixed group was composed of two individuals who were liked by one other member of the group, and one who was disliked by one other member of the group. The fourth subject did not choose or reject, nor was he chosen or rejected by, the other group members.

Each of the three groups met for five sessions, each 45 minutes long, to discuss one of five topics structured to be of interest to medical students. The topics were assigned in counterbalanced order.

Sound film recordings were made of each of the 15 sessions from the observation room, and continuous and synchronous recordings of the GSR responses of each subject were collected.

The GSR was exosomatically recorded after the manner of Edelberg and Burch (1962). Two GSR parameters were considered in subsequent analysis: the frequency of GSR deflection and the amplitude measured as the height of the deflection from onset to peak.

The GSR was recorded through an amplifier that had a time constant of 8 seconds, and a transient change was counted as a GSR only if the amplitude of the change was greater than 0.1 per cent of the subject's initial basal resistance. Basal resistance did not change appreciably in any subject throughout a single run, and showed a fairly constant level from session to session in most subjects. The basal resistance throughout the subject population ranged from a low of 9K to a high of 110K. The definition of GSR as a percentage change of the basal resistance is a first-approximation correction factor for the direct correlation that exists between amplitude of GSR and level of basal resistance.

The sound film recordings were coded in terms of Bales's (1951) 12 interaction process categories.

Analysis. With Spearman's rank-order coefficient as the measure of association, and the minute as the varying time unit, the number and amplitude of GSR deflections of each subject were correlated with the number and amplitude of the GSR deflections of each of the other group members; the number of his own responses in each of the 12 categories, and his total responses, regardless of the person to whom they were addressed; and the number of his responses in each of the categories, and his total responses, *directed toward each other person in the group.*

The specific questions deriving from the general hypotheses were posed in terms of the relative probability of obtaining positive correlations of .29 or above in one sociometric grouping as opposed to another, using chi-square analysis to test the relationship.*

A positive correlation for GSR in a 1-minute sample was taken as obtaining if either one or both of the GSR parameters of a subject

---

* It is of particular importance to appreciate that the use of Spearman's rank-order coefficient in Study I and Pearson's product-moment correlation in Study II is not related to determining level of significance, but rather to establishing the nominal class "positive correlation" between various parameters of 1-minute or ½-minute sample durations. The chi-square test has been employed to determine level of significance of the difference between the class "positive correlation above .29 magnitude" as compared with the other class of this universe "correlation below .29 magnitude" as both classes are distributed in the three different sociometric groups. It should be noted that events within a class are not ordered.

correlated above the predetermined magnitude with either one or both GSR parameters of another subject.

The subjects met in four-man groups but, for present purposes, the paired affective relationship was chosen as the unit of analysis. The positive group consisted of six pairs in reciprocal "liking" relationship. The negative group consisted of three negative pairs (at least one member of each pair disliked the other pair member) and three neutral pairs (the pair members indicated neither like nor dislike for each other). The mixed group consisted of one unilateral positive, one unilateral negative, and four neutral pairs. Combining the similar relationships for the three groups, there were seven positive, four negative, and seven neutral pairs for each of the five sessions (a total of 90 relationships).

Results. The major hypothesis of the study was that physiological covariation was more likely to occur among pair members who had a strong affective (positive or negative) orientation toward each other than among pair members who neither liked nor disliked each other. The results pertaining to this hypothesis are reproduced in Table 1.

The general hypothesis was confirmed, since positive and negative relationships combined were significantly more likely to manifest physiological covariation than neutral relationships ($\chi^2 = 5.6$, $p < .02$). However, an extremely important finding, not predicted by the general hypothesis, was that this difference was due to the weight that the negative pairs contributed. The negative pairs were

TABLE 1

Correlations of GSR Responses of Pair Members: Study 1

| | Pairs | | | | | |
| | Negative | | Positive | | Neutral | |
Correlations	N	%	N	%	N	%
Positive correlations above .29 between GSR responses of pair members	15	75	13	37	9	26
Correlations below .29 between GSR responses of pair members	5	25	22	63	26	74
Total	20	100	35	100	35	100

Values of χ^2 and p: affective (positive and negative) vs. neutral, $\chi^2 = 5.6$, $p < .02$; negative vs. positive, $\chi^2 = 7.3$, $p < .01$; negative vs. neutral, $\chi^2 = 12.5$, $p < .001$; positive vs. neutral, χ^2 n.s.

significantly more likely to manifest physiological covariation than either the positive ($\chi^2 = 7.3$, $p < .01$) or the neutral ($\chi^2 = 12.5$, $p < .001$) pairs; and there was *no* significant difference between the positive and neutral pairs in the tendency of the pair members to co-vary physiologically. These findings are of special significance when considered in conjunction with those summarized in Table 2.

TABLE 2

Correlations of Subject's GSR with his Own Categorized and Total Social Responses Directed toward Negative, Positive, and Neutral Objects: Study 1

	Objects					
	Negative		Positive		Neutral	
Correlations	N	%	N	%	N	%
Positive GSR correlations above .29 with own categorized and total social responses	46	22	86	22	59	14
GSR correlations below .29 with own categorized and total social responses	164	78	304	78	364	86
Total	210	100	390	100	423	100

Values of χ^2 and p: affective (positive and negative) vs. neutral, $\chi^2 = 10.6$, $p < .005$; negative vs. neutral, $\chi^2 = 6.4$, $p < .02$; positive vs. neutral, $\chi^2 = 9.1$, $p < .005$; negative vs. positive, χ^2 n.s.

The results in Table 2 were derived by correlating the GSR parameters in a 1-minute sample of each subject with his own responses in each of Bales's categories, and with his own total responses, *that were directed toward each other individual in the group.* When comparing the number of positive correlations that derived from behavior directed toward positive or negative social objects as compared with neutral social objects it was found that correlations between GSR and acts directed toward people in positive ($\chi^2 = 9.1$, $p < .005$) or in negative ($\chi^2 = 6.4$, $p < .02$) relationships were significantly more likely to occur than correlations between GSR and acts directed toward neutral social objects. There was *no* significant difference in the number of positive correlations between GSR and interactions when positive and negative relationships were compared.

Thus, members of positive and negative pairs are *equally* likely to manifest positive correlations between their GSR responses and their acts directed toward their partners; and both are more likely to manifest such correlations than members of neutral pairs. However, members of negative pairs are significantly more likely to *covary physiologically* than members of either positive or neutral pairs.

The above results suggest that a member of a negative pair is autonomically activated by his own acts—primarily socioemotional (Kaplan *et al.*, 1963)—directed toward a partner, and is also activated by his partner's acts directed toward him, while a member of a positive pair is activated only by his own acts directed toward his partner. Members of neutral pairs do not tend to be autonomically activated, even by their own acts. Such a hierarchy of autonomic response in relation to socioemotional interaction must represent different degrees and levels of communication between members of the small group. The information content of an act or verbalization may be, to a considerable extent, a function of the affect relationship existing between the "transmitter" and "receiver." We have previously suggested (Kaplan *et al.*, 1963) that the greater incidence of physiological covariation among members of negative pairs might be an indication of their heightened sensitivity to each other's activity, perhaps on the basis of mutually perceived threat. At the very least it would seem that the negative-pair member must overdetermine the productions of his partner and autonomically overrespond to them in relation to the productions of other members.

If this interpretation of "distortion" of communication by strong affect relationships is tenable, then it is to be expected that in dyadic relationships negative-pair members not only would behave but also would subjectively characterize their behavior in a way that was different from positive- and neutral-pair members. The next study was undertaken to investigate such subjective characterizations and to verify the findings of the first study with respect to physiological covariation.

There were three major limitations to the study reported above. First, only three groups meeting over five sessions were utilized. Second, in our analysis we treated the dyadic relationship as if in isolation, when in fact it was a component of a larger group. Third, we failed to demonstrate that differential *perception* of the interpersonal transactions was a function of sociometric object choice.

In the second study the number of groups was increased, the subjects met in two-person groups, and data were collected on the differential subjective perceptions of the social process.

Study 2

Method. The subjects were chosen from a third-year class of 54 female nursing students. A sociometric questionnaire was administered to the group, in which each student was asked to indicate her feelings toward each of her classmates along a 5-point scale ranging from "strong feeling of liking" to "strong feeling of disliking," while bearing in mind the degree of similarity of each classmate to the person the subject "liked most" and the person the subject "liked least" in the world. The midpoint on the scale indicated neither liking nor disliking. The subjects were also asked to indicate their perceptions of how each of their classmates felt toward them along the same scale.

At the same time the subjects responded to an 18-item opinion questionnaire, indicating their degree of agreement or disagreement (along a 5-point scale) with various statements concerning current events, social problems, and the feminine role.

Ten positive, eleven neutral, and ten negative pairs were chosen on the basis of the sociometric data. The positive pairs were composed of two subjects each of whom indicated extreme liking for her partner and perceived her partner as having strong feelings of liking for her. The neutral pairs consisted of subjects each of whom indicated that she neither liked nor disliked her partner and that her partner neither liked nor disliked her. For the complement of negative pairs we were unable to find ten pairs that would fit the predetermined criteria perfectly, that is, in which each subject expressed strong feelings of dislike toward her partner and perceived her partner as having strong feelings of dislike toward her. However, eight pairs were found that did conform to these criteria. The other two negative pairs consisted of subjects each of whom indicated neither liking nor disliking for her partner *but* perceived her partner as having strong feelings of dislike for her.

Each pair met for two successive 20-minute discussion sessions. For one of the sessions the subjects were assigned a topic about which they held the *same* strong opinion (as determined by the previously administered 18-item questionnaire). The subjects were asked to discuss the reasons for their similar opinions. For the second of the two discussions the subjects were assigned a topic about which they held strong but *opposing* opinions. The subjects were asked to discuss the reasons for their disagreement, resolve their differences, and come to a common conclusion. Half the pairs received the former instructions first and half received the latter instructions first.

For purposes of the present analysis the "same" and "opposing" discussions were combined for all pairs, since an examination of the perceptual data revealed no significant differences between the two discussion conditions.

For all sessions, continuous and synchronous GSR recordings were collected for each subject, by the same method as in Study 1.

At the end of the two-session sequence the subjects filled out an instrument consisting of ten statements descriptive of role behavior in group interaction. The respondents ranked the statements to indicate which of these statements was most descriptive of role behavior in group interaction. The respondents ranked the statements to indicate which of these statements was most descriptive of their own (and their partner's) behavior for each discussion session, and which were least descriptive of their own (and their partner's) behavior. The schedule upon which the present instrument is based is reported in Stock and Thelen (1958, pp. 265–66). Certain of the items of the revised instrument appear in Table 4.

Analysis. The major purpose of this investigation was to provide data relevant to a description of the relationship between physiological covariation and sociometric relationship, and between sociometric relationship and the subjects' perceptions of their own (and their partners') social behavior.

Physiological covariation was defined in terms of the product-moment correlation between the number of GSR deflections per half-minute of the pair members. The first relationship was described in terms of the relative probability of obtaining significant positive correlations (greater than .30, $p < .05$) for members of negative pairs when compared with positive- and neutral-pair members, using chi-square analysis to test the relationship.

To describe the second relationship, the procedure was as follows. For each of the descriptive behavioral statements, the distribution of the subjects' rankings of that statement as it applied to their own (and their partners') behavior was as nearly as possible divided into "high" and "low" categories. The negative-, positive-, and neutral-pair members were then compared to determine if there were any significant differences between these groups with respect to the distribution of high and low ranks on each statement, again using chi-square analysis to test the relationships.

Results. The data relevant to the first relationship are summarized in Table 3. When comparing the number of significant positive correlations between the GSR responses of pair members for negative pairs with the number obtained for positive and neutral pairs, we found that negative pairs were significantly more likely to yield such correlations than either positive ($\chi^2 = 7.0, p < .01$) or neutral ($\chi^2 = 6.2, p < .02$) pairs. These results confirm those of the first study, in which it was found that physiological covariation was significantly more likely to occur between negative-pair members than between positive- and neutral-pair members.

TABLE 3

Correlations of GSR Responses of Pair Members

| | Pairs | | | | | |
| | Negative | | Positive | | Neutral | |
Correlations	N	%	N	%	N	%
Positive correlations above .30 between GSR responses of pair members	11	55	3	15	4	18
Correlations below .30 between GSR responses of pair members	9	45	17	85	18	82
Total	20	100	20	100	22	100

Values of χ^2 and p: negative vs. positive, $\chi^2 = 7.0$, $p < .01$; negative vs. neutral, $\chi^2 = 6.2$, $p < .02$; positive vs. neutral, χ^2 n.s.

When examining the data relevant to the second relationship, we found that sociometric groupings were significantly related to self and partner rankings on four of the statements descriptive of social behavior. These results are summarized in Table 4. Since each pair met for two sessions, the total of *individual* subjective rankings of each statement for the negative, positive, and neutral pairs should have been 40, 40, and 44, respectively. (The N of 32 for negative-pair members results from the failure of the members of two pairs to fill out the appropriate instrument.)

Distributions of High and Low Ranks on Statements Descriptive of Self and Partner by Sociometric Grouping: Study 2

		Pair Members						χ^2			
Statement	Rank	Negative N	%	Positive N	%	Neutral N	%	All groups (d.f. = 2)	Negative vs. positive (d.f. = 1)	Negative vs. neutral (d.f. = 1)	Positive vs. neutral (d.f. = 1)
"I was especially warm and friendly to my partner."	High	10	31	26	65	21	48	8.2 ($p < .02$)	8.1 ($p < .005$)	n.s. ($p < .10$)	n.s.
	Low	22	69	14	35	23	52				
	Total	32	100	40	100	44	100				
"She (my partner) was especially warm and friendly to me."	High	12	38	31	78	25	57	11.8 ($p < .005$)	11.8 ($p < .001$)	2.8 ($p < .10$)	4.0 ($p < .05$)
	Low	20	62	9	22	19	43				
	Total	32	100	40	100	44	100				
"I did not participate much."	High	14	44	19	48	31	70	6.7 ($p < .05$)	n.s.	5.5 ($p < .02$)	4.6 ($p < .05$)
	Low	18	56	21	52	13	30				
	Total	32	100	40	100	44	100				
"She (my partner) did not participate much."	High	8	25	21	52	25	57	8.4 ($p < .02$)	5.6 ($p < .02$)	7.6 ($p < .01$)	n.s.
	Low	24	75	19	48	19	43				
	Total	32	100	40	100	44	100				
"I was polite to my partner."	High	17	53	14	35	33	75	13.6 ($p < .005$)	n.s.	3.9 ($p < .05$)	13.6 ($p < .005$)
	Low	15	47	26	65	11	25				
	Total	32	100	40	100	44	100				
"She (my partner) was polite to me."	High	16	50	15	38	31	70	9.3 ($p < .01$)	n.s.	3.3 ($p < .10$)	9.2 ($p < .005$)
	Low	16	50	25	62	13	30				
	Total	32	100	40	100	44	100				
"I was eager and aggressive."	High	21	66	21	52	11	25	13.4 ($p < .005$)	n.s.	12.5 ($p < .001$)	6.7 ($p < .01$)
	Low	11	34	19	48	33	75				
	Total	32	100	40	100	44	100				
"She (my partner) was eager and aggressive."	High	21	66	19	48	17	39	5.4 ($p < .10$)	n.s.	5.4 ($p = .02$)	n.s.
	Low	11	34	21	52	27	61				
	Total	32	100	40	100	44	100				

The sociometric groupings were most significantly related to the subjects' ratings of self and partner on four statements—those referring to warmth and friendliness, participation, politeness, and eagerness and aggression. The relationships in seven of the eight cases were significant at the .05 level or better.

There was a positive relationship between the perception of self ($\chi^2 = 8.2, p < .02$) and partner ($\chi^2 = 11.8, p < .005$) as being warm and friendly during the discussion and sociometric grouping. Positive-pair members were most likely to perceive themselves and their partners as being "especially warm and friendly," negative-pair members were least likely to do so, and neutral-pair members fell between. *Thus the initial expressions of liking and disliking on the sociometric questionnaire were shown to parallel the differential perceptions of warmth and friendliness during interaction.*

The significant relationship between perception of one's own ($\chi^2 = 6.7, p < .05$) and one's partner's ($\chi^2 = 8.4, p < .02$) participation took a somewhat different form. The negative-pair members were least likely to indicate that they (and their partners) did *not* participate very much, the neutral-pair members were most likely to do so, and the positive-pair members were in between in this regard.

The significant relationship between perceptions of one's own ($\chi^2 = 13.6, p < .005$) and one's partner's ($\chi^2 = 9.3, p < .01$) politeness took the following form. Neutral-pair members were most likely to perceive themselves and their partners as being polite, positive-pair members were least likely to do so, and negative-pair members were moderately so inclined.

Finally, there was a significant relationship between perception of self ($\chi^2 = 13.4, p < .005$) and partner ($\chi^2 = 5.4, p < .10$) with respect to being "eager and aggressive." Negative-pair members were most likely to indicate that they and their partners were eager and aggressive, neutral-pair members were least likely to do so, and positive-pair members were moderate in this regard.

Since negative pairs were significantly more likely to manifest physiological covariation than either the positive or the neutral groups, individual comparisons were made between the former and each of the latter.

Negative-pair members when compared with positive-pair members were significantly *less* likely to regard themselves ($\chi^2 = 8.1,$

$p < .005$) and their partners ($\chi^2 = 11.8$, $p < .001$) as being warm and friendly, and were significantly less likely to perceive their partners as not participating ($\chi^2 = 5.6$, $p < .02$).

Negative-pair members, when compared with neutral-pair members, were less likely to perceive their partners as being warm and friendly ($\chi^2 = 2.8$, $p < .10$); less likely to perceive themselves ($\chi^2 = 5.5$, $p < .02$) and their partners ($\chi^2 = 7.6$, $p < .01$) as not participating very much; less likely to indicate that they ($\chi^2 = 3.9$, $p < .05$) and their partners ($\chi^2 = 3.3$, $p < .10$) were polite; and *more* likely to view themselves ($\chi^2 = 12.5$, $p < .001$) and their partners ($\chi^9 - 5.4$, $p = .02$) as eager and aggressive.

Certain rather strong parallels between the results of the objective categorical coding used in Study 1 and the subjective descriptions of social behavior used in Study 2, should be noted.

With respect to participation, the present study indicated that positive- and negative-pair members were less likely than neutral-pair members to indicate that they did not participate, and negative-pair members were quite similar to positive-pair members in this regard. Parallel findings were noted in Study 1. In the negative and positive groups the mean numbers of acts produced per session were 948 and 954, respectively, as compared with 895 for the neutral group. Thus, in both studies positive- and negative-group members were similarly more active than neutral-pair members.

Parallel findings were also noted for the content of the interaction. In the second study it was noted that both negative- and positive-pair members were significantly more likely to perceive themselves as eager and aggressive than were neutral-pair members, and the difference between the positive- and negative-pair members was not significant, although the negative-pair members showed a slightly greater tendency in this regard. Similarly, in the first study, when considering the proportions of total acts that were *actively* negative (disagreement and antagonism), we found that both the negative and the positive groups manifested a slightly higher proportion of such acts than the neutral group.

Another parallel between the two studies is provided by the proportion of "joking" responses by the various groups in Study 1. The positive group had a higher proportion of such responses than the negative or neutral groups. This result may be taken as analogous to the finding in Study 2 that the positive-pair members perceived themselves and their partners as being warm and friendly to a greater extent than the negative- or the neutral-pair members.

Finally, there are a number of similarities between the perceptions of the neutral-pair members in Study 2 and the behaviors of the corresponding group in Study 1. Neutral-pair members in Study 2 were morely likely to perceive themselves and their partners as being polite and non-participating, and less likely to perceive themselves as eager and aggressive than the positive- and negative-pair members. Again, parallels with the first study are suggested in that the neutral group had a greater proportion of "withdrawal" responses relative to the other two groups, fewer total acts, and proportionately fewer actively negative acts than the positive or negative groups.

To summarize the results of the two studies, then, sociometric groupings were shown to be related to both physiological covariation and the patterns of social behavior in small peer groups.

In both studies, members of negative pairs were significantly more likely to covary physiologically than members of either positive or neutral pairs.

Sociometric groupings were also differentiated in terms of their patterns of interpersonal behavior as indicated by objective coding (Study 1) and by subjective characterizations (Study 2). The three sociometric groupings may be described as follows. (1) Negative-group members were characterized by high participation and highly aggressive behavior underlying which were strong feelings of hostility for their partners. (2) Positive-pair members were also active and aggressive, but underlying these patterns of behavior were feelings of warmth and friendliness. (3) Neutral-pair members were characterized by affective neutrality and a relatively low degree of participation.

Discussion

We have interpreted the index of physiological covariation as a measure of the degree of simultaneous and consensual affective investment in the stimulus field by the participants in social interaction. That is, to the extent that the coparticipants are simultaneously alerted or oriented to stimuli that are jointly meaningful (whether the stimulus is positively cathected, threatening, or merely a novel intrusion into the environment) they will both manifest a higher level of physiological activation, and to the extent that the current environment is *jointly* perceived as tension-reducing *or* "meaningless," both participants will manifest a lower level of physiological activation. Insofar as they thus commonly perceive variations in the stimulus field over time, they will manifest a higher degree of physiological covariation. Conversely, to the extent that the environment evokes different degrees of meaning or affect, the participants will manifest lesser degrees of physiological covariation, and presumably to the extent that the environment is tension-reducing for one and tension-inducing for the other, they will manifest a higher *negative* correlation between their physiological responses.

The interpretation of the index of physiological covariation presented above appears to be warranted upon consideration of the data collected from these two studies. Physiological covariation certainly cannot be accounted for only by such factors as amount of activity, simultaneity of social acts, or overt expression of negative affect.

In both studies the negative pairs were significantly more likely to manifest physiological covariation than positive pairs. Yet there were no appreciable differences between these groups with respect to the total number of acts produced (Study 1) or to the subjects' perceptions of their degree of participation (Study 2).

Again, if simultaneity of social responses were to account for the degree of physiological covariation, then we would expect the negative pairs to yield higher positive correlations between the total number of acts of the pair members per time unit than neutral or positive pairs. However, in Study 1 we found that negative pairs yielded on the average higher *negative* correlations ($-.27$) between the acts per minute between pair members than the neutral ($-.24$) and positive ($-.16$) pairs.

Finally, even such a variable as the extent of overt negativity cannot account for degree of physiological covariation over time. While negative-pair members were significantly more likely to manifest physiological covariation than positive-pair members, there was no significant difference between them with respect either to the proportion of acts that were overtly negative (Study 1) or to the subjects' perception of "eagerness and aggression" (Study 2). However, the differential degree of physiological covariation can be accounted for in terms of the mutual affective orientation that characterized the relationship. In the studies presented above, the significantly greater tendency of negative-pair members to covary physiologically is apparently the result of their relatively greater sensitivity to their own and their partners' behavior. The major differences between the negative-pair members and *both* the positive- and the neutral-pair members (Study 2) were with respect to the degree of warmth and friendliness and the extent of participation attributed to their partners (Table 4). Negative-pair members were least likely to perceive their partners as warm and friendly and to perceive their partners as *not* participating very much. A further indication of the greater sensitivity of the negative-pair members to each other's behavior is the greater differential between perceptions of their own and their partners' participation. While there was no significant difference between the negative- and the positive-pair members with respect to the perception of their own participation, there was a significant difference ($p < .02$) with respect to their perception of their *partners'* participation.

In view of the fact that our general hypothesis (Study 1), failed to predict the observed difference in physiological covariation between the positive and negative pairs, it is of interest to consider two possible interpretations of this finding. First, there was a general tendency in both studies for the respondents from which the subjects were chosen to make a greater number of positive than negative choices. Hence the few negative choices that were made may reflect a greater intensity of affect. Second, it is possible that under the conditions of the present study the behavior of the subjects was not sufficiently threatening to the relationship to be of common significance. Under conditions of greater competition, for example, positive-pair members might be more likely to covary physiologically than neutral-pair members.

In any case, however, the results strongly suggest that a measure of physiological covariation may be used as an index of consensual affective investment in the study of social interaction.

REFERENCES

Bales, R. F. *Interaction process analysis.* Cambridge, Mass.: Addison-Wesley, 1951.
Coleman, R., Greenblatt, M., and Solomon, H. C. Physiological evidence of rapport during psychotherapeutic interviews. *Dis. nerv. System,* 1956, **17,** 2–8.

Davis, R. C. Physiological responses as a means of evaluating information. In A. D. Biderman and H. Zimmer (Eds.), *The manipulation of human behavior*. New York: Wiley, 1961. Pp. 142–68.

DiMascio, A., Boyd, R. W., Greenblatt, M., and Solomon, H. C. The psychiatric interview: a sociophysiologic study. *Dis. nerv. System*, 1955, **16**, 2–7.

DiMascio, A., Boyd, R. W., and Greenblatt, M. Physiological correlates of tension and antagonism during psychotherapy. A study of "interpersonal physiology." *Psychosom. Med.*, 1957, **19**, 99–104.

Edelberg, R., and Burch, N. R. Skin resistance and galvanic skin response (influence of surface variables, and methodological implications). *A.M.A. Arch. gen. Psychiat.*, 1962, **7**, 163–69.

Horwitz, M. The veridicality of liking and disliking. In R. Tagiuri and L. Petrullo (Eds.), *Person perception and interpersonal behavior*. Stanford, Calif.: Stanford Univ. Press, 1958. Pp. 191–209.

Kaplan, H. B., Burch, N. R., Bloom, S. W., and Edelberg, R. Affective orientation and physiological activity (GSR) in small peer groups. *Psychosom. Med.*, 1963, **25**, 245–52.

Lacey, J. I. Psychophysiological approaches to the evaluation of psychotherapeutic process and outcome. In *Research in psychotherapy*, Washington, D.C.: American Psychological Association, 1959. Pp. 160–208.

Lindzey, G., and Borgatta, E. F. Sociometric measurement. In G. Lindzey (Ed.), *Handbook of social psychology*. Cambridge, Mass.: Addison-Wesley, 1954. Pp. 405–48.

Malmo, R. B., Boag, T. J., and Smith, A. A. Physiological study of personal interaction. *Psychosom. Med.*, 1957, **19**, 105–119.

Martin, Irene. Somatic reactivity. In H. J. Eysenck (Ed.), *Handbook of abnormal psychology*. New York: Basic Books, 1961. Pp. 417–56.

Stock, Dorothy, and Thelen, H. A. *Emotional dynamics and group culture*. New York: New York Univ. Press, 1958.

Thibaut, J. W., and Kelley, H. H. *The social psychology of groups*. New York: Wiley, 1959.

Acts and Activation: A Psychophysiological Study of Social Interaction

DAVID SHAPIRO AND P. HERBERT LEIDERMAN*
Harvard Medical School

Introduction

In a previous paper we demonstrated that behavioral and physiological techniques can be used in the experimental analysis of group interaction (Leiderman and Shapiro, 1963). The aim of this paper is to explore further the proposition that the relationships between the physiological and behavioral responses vary with the type of social setting.

The choice of physiological measures appropriate in the study of group behavior is somewhat arbitrary. We were guided by the following criteria: the measures should be sensitive to relatively subtle changes in the social and psychological environment, and they should have temporal characteristics of the same order of magnitude as the behavior. They should be easily recorded throughout the experiment without interfering with the interaction. Finally, they should reflect a continuous response of the individual not readily observable by other persons in his presence.

Of the many possible variables that meet these criteria, two were selected, galvanic skin potential level (GSP) and heart rate (HR).

This work was supported by Contract Nonr-1866(43), Office of Naval Research (Group Psychology Branch); Career Investigator Award M-2276, U.S. Public Health Service (NIMH); Research Career Development Award K3-MH-20, 476-01, U.S. Public Health Service (NIMH); Research Grant M-4209, U.S. Public Health Service (NIMH). Subsidized use of time on the Harvard University computing equipment was made possible by National Science Foundation Grant GP-683 to the Computing Center. We also acknowledge the use of facilities at the Massachusetts Institute of Technology Computation Center in Cambridge, Mass. The work was done at the Massachusetts Mental Health Center, Harvard Medical School, Boston, Mass.
* P. Herbert Leiderman is now at the Stanford University School of Medicine.

Lacey, Bateman, and VanLehn (1953), Mandler *et al.* (1961), and Shapiro and Leiderman (1964), demonstrate that these indices have low correlation.

Galvanic skin potential level is assumed to be an index of activation and is probably related to central nervous system (CNS) arousal (Woodworth and Schlosberg, 1954). Following Malmo (1962), we conceive of GSP as indicating the "intensive" dimension of experience, without differentiation of such subjective states as fear and joy. The GSP level varies significantly with such behavioral states as sleep, alert wakefulness, and activity in a simple task (Leiderman and Shapiro, 1964). Compared with GSP, HR is probably less directly responsive to changes in the external environment and more directly associated with internal physiological regulation, at least under conditions of mild or moderate stress.

Conceptualization of the relationship between autonomic and performance variables is certainly rudimentary. Our previous work suggests that a high rate of activity may be accompanied by either high or low levels of physiological activation. Such factors as social setting and reinforcement, time and experience in a situation, and habituation of response influence the relationship. For example, in a learning task performed by an individual alone, Morningstar (1963) found that amount of reinforced activity was inversely related to activation as measured by GSP. Other findings suggest that the level of activation is increased when tasks are performed in a group.

We hypothesized that the social nature of activity in initiating group decisions, when such activity is rewarded, would be characterized by high levels of activation. We expected that the same kind of activity in a non-rewarded social role would be accompanied by a low state of arousal. Other considerations, such as set or expectancy, might also operate, especially where arousal level and behavior were not congruent.

Procedure

The subjects were third-year student nurses, who were paid $1.50 an hour. Groups of three were brought into the experimental room by a female technician who attached the electrodes. The laboratory was 9 × 13 feet, sound-attenuated, light- and temperature-controlled, with a one-way vision screen. Physiological data were recorded on an

8-channel Offner Type R dynograph. Each session consisted of a 15-minute initial rest period, an experimental period of 40 minutes, and a final 15-minute rest period.

The experimental task was a contrived game in which the subjects as a group were required to guess the order of colors on the experimenter's list. Unknown to the subjects, there was no list of colors.

The instructions were as follows:

Now we want you to take part in a guessing game. This is how it works. In the other room I have a long list of colors written down, and you have to guess each color on my list and try to get as many right as possible.

Your job is to talk it over with each other and decide what the color is each time. As you do, please discuss how you arrived at your decision, and also name the color you are going to choose for each guess. Speak distinctly so that you can be understood. As soon as all three of you agree on a color, you stop talking and turn on the light by pressing the button of the color on the box in front of you. All three buttons have to be down for the light to go on. You keep the light on until you find out whether you guessed right or wrong. If you guessed right, you will hear a sound like this (tone). If you guessed wrong, you will hear a sound like this (buzzer). As soon as you find out how you did, turn off the light. Whether you guessed right or wrong, I'll go on to the next color on my list and you have to guess that one. It may be the same color as the last one, or it may be different.

The subjects were then given a few practice trials. The tone or buzzer was sounded five seconds after each decision. The tone was pleasant-sounding and the buzzer harsh-sounding. The intensity of both sounds was 72 decibels, and they lasted 1.5 seconds.

We use such terms as "reinforcement," "success," and "reward" as equivalents for "right" (tone). The terms "non-reinforcement," "failure," and "non-reward" are likewise interchangeable with "wrong" (buzzer). Success and failure were manipulated by the experimenter following procedures to be described below.

The groups were free to respond at their own rate. For any one trial, the initiator was defined as the subject who first suggested the color that the group chose as its decision. The initiation rate ($\bar{x}$ Init) for each subject was the mean number of times per minute during the entire experiment that she was the one who initiated the group's decisions. Judgments of this behavior were made easily and reliably.

Turning to the physiological variables, GSP was measured as the potential difference between an active area on the thenar eminence of the left palm and an inactive area on the dorsal aspect of the left forearm. The continuous GSP level was sampled at 1-minute intervals and treated as a slowly-changing function; responses occurring faster than once a minute were ignored. A single sample in a 1-minute interval is typically within a mV of the mean of 30 samples in the same interval. The sampled values were averaged ($\bar{x}$ GSP) to describe the level over a period of elapsed time. In our data analysis, difference scores ($\Delta\bar{x}$ GSP) between the mean level of the initial rest period and the mean level during the total experimental period were taken as an index of the experimental effect. There is no correlation between $\Delta\bar{x}$ GSP and initial resting level. These difference scores compensate for variations in pre-experimental resting levels as a function of individual differences, over-all group differences, and time factors.*

Heart rate was recorded from peripheral leads placed bilaterally on the upper arms and was measured by counting the number of beats per 12-second block of time at each successive minute. This value multiplied by five was the estimate of heart rate for the minute. The sampled values per period of elapsed time were then used to compute the mean heart rate ($\bar{x}$ HR).† Difference scores ($\Delta\bar{x}$ HR), as for GSP, were used in the analysis of change in HR level. We have assumed that there is no relationship between initial resting level and these difference scores in the range of HR levels studied.

Our study consisted of two major group reinforcement conditions and a third control condition for comparison. In the first two conditions, group success and failure were made contingent on the roles taken by specific subjects in initiating decisions. In the third, social roles were allowed to evolve spontaneously.

We called the first condition *monadic* leadership; in this condition a successful outcome for the group was possible only if *one particular subject,* designated in advance, initiated the decision. The second condition was named *dyadic* leadership; here success hinged on the initiation by *either one of two* of the three subjects. In a third condition, *natural* leadership, success and failure followed a random sched-

---

* A discussion of some statistical properties of GSP as used in this study may be found in Shapiro and Leiderman (1964) ; $\bar{x}$ GSP is normally distributed, has a low positive correlation with variance, is highly consistent within a session, and is relatively consistent on different occasions under the same experimental conditions.

† The average algebraic difference between $\bar{x}$ HR based on the 12-second block compared with the total number of beats, for three subjects in a 70-minute experiment, was less than .65 beats per minute, approximately 1 per cent error.

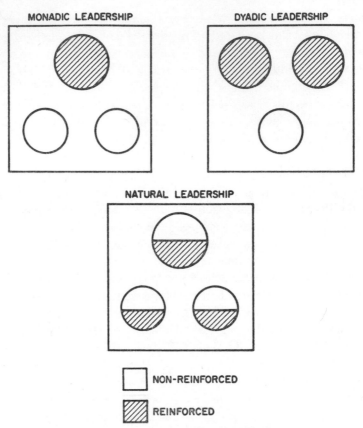

Fig. 1. Leadership and role conditions.

ule, so that the chance that a subject could lead the group to success was one in three. In this case, group reinforcement was *not* contingent on the interaction of subjects in making decisions, and roles were not manipulated.

Figure 1 shows the leadership and role conditions. In the case of *monadic* leadership, there was a single reinforced role, while the other two individuals shared non-reinforced roles. In the case of *dyadic* leadership, two subjects shared reinforced roles, while the third or non-reinforced role was unique in the group. In *natural* leadership, the subject actually initiating most decisions was arbitrarily designated the "high-response" role, while the other two subjects constituted the "low-response" roles.

The data on *monadic* leadership were obtained from five groups of three subjects. Each group was run in three successive sessions in which the reinforced role was alternated from subject to subject. For the *dyadic* leadership condition, 12 groups of subjects were run, each for a single experimental session. However, all of the 51 subjects had two prior experiences in the laboratory. In the first, they performed the same experimental task individually under a random reinforcement schedule, while their second experience was in a group, also under conditions of random reinforcement. The latter constituted the *natural* leadership condition.*

Although the different groups of subjects varied in their approaches to the task, the over-all level of involvement was the same from condition to condition. Subjects found the game intriguing; the search for a pattern in the presumed list of colors was especially challenging. A run of successful guesses seemed to accelerate behavior and increase excitement, apparently suggesting the possibility that a simple solution to the problem was being discovered. When the subjects achieved continued success, however, the task became routine. Failure was frustrating; it sometimes made subjects feel annoyed, as several remarked in post-experimental interviews. The buzzer meaning "wrong" was considered quite unpleasant. In several instances of repeated failure, subjects appeared to become apathetic about the game, and to exert less effort, without actually withdrawing completely. Similarly, successive experience in the laboratory led to a decline in overt expression of interest. We shall assume for our present purposes that the findings to be presented are based on the differential manipulation of role within each leadership situation.

In the analysis of data, we shall try to answer the following questions:

1. How does the nature of the leadership situation influence behavioral and physiological changes?

2. How do behavioral and physiological responses vary within the experimentally contrived roles?

Behavioral Results

Table 1 presents the behavioral data for individual roles and for groups as units in each situation. The total group output of initiations

* For this purpose, two groups were omitted where no single subject was clearly a major initiator of decisions, making a total of 15 groups in this condition.

was approximately equivalent in the three group conditions, though the activity of subjects relative to one another changed considerably as a function of the reinforcement procedure. Differences in $\bar{x}$ Init in the four roles in the *monadic* and *dyadic* leadership conditions were at the .10 level (Median Test). The largest difference was found between reinforced and non-reinforced roles within the *monadic* situation ($p < .05$).

TABLE 1

Mean Values of $\bar{x}$ Initiations
(responses/min)

| | Individual Performance | | | |
| Leadership condition | Role | No. of subjects | Initiation rate | |
			$\bar{x}$	s
Monadic	Reinforced	15	1.6	1.05
	Non-reinforced	30	0.6	.35
Dyadic	Reinforced	24	1.0	.48
	Non-reinforced	12	0.8	.35
Natural	High-response	15	1.2	.52
	Low-response	30	0.7	.26

| | Total Group Performance | | |
| Leadership condition | No. of groups | Initiation rate | |
		$\bar{x}$	s
Monadic	15	2.8	.81
Dyadic	12	2.9	.60
Natural	15	2.6	.66

The effectiveness of the experimental manipulation of roles may be evaluated by inspecting the *natural* leadership data. Under conditions of partial reward, the spontaneous leaders (high responses) initiated almost as many decisions as the subjects in reinforced roles. Thus, the created roles in which subjects were arbitrarily selected to fulfill a particular social function approximated the behavioral conditions of "natural" leadership. Note that the *monadic* reinforced role generated more responses than the natural leadership role; this demonstrates that leadership behavior can be manipulated by reinforcement.

Since there were three successive *monadic* sessions, we shall examine leadership trends, taking sequence into account. The percentage of initiations for the reinforced role increased from 37 per cent to 62 per cent to 72 per cent of the total group initiation rate with the successive experience of the group in the three experimental situations. Although subjects varied in their amount of initiated activity, the leadership role was effectively transferred from one subject to the next in successive sessions. In other words, the groups adapted to the change in reinforcement contingencies over time and with experience in the task, seemingly overriding individual propensities.

Physiological Results

Given the experimentally contrived roles, we asked whether they would bear any systematic relationship to the physiological variables. Since the HR data showed no trends that helped differentiate the experimental conditions, they will not be presented in detail.

Impressive results were obtained for GSP, as shown in Fig. 2. The $\Delta \bar{x}$ GSP values for each subject are also given in Table 2.

Differences in $\Delta \bar{x}$ GSP for the four major roles were statistically significant ($p < .05$, Median Test). The *dyadic* reinforced role yielded the largest increase in GSP, an average of 5.3 mV. This dual role was characterized by a high rate of reinforced social activity in a situation also having the greatest amount of over-all reinforcement. In contrast, the non-reinforced role in this situation showed a decrease in $\bar{x}$ GSP.

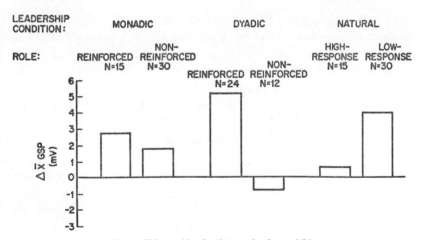

Fig. 2. Effect of leadership and role on GSP.

TABLE 2

Individual Δx̄ GSP Values

(R = Reinforced; NR = Non-reinforced)

Monadic Leadership*			Dyadic Leadership			Natural Leadership		
						High-response	Low-response	
R	NR(1)	NR(2)	R(1)	R(2)	NR		(1)	(2)
8.3	4.3	-7.2†	-8.1	3.3	-6.9	2.4	-1.3	4.2
1.0	-9.8	-13.2	0.0	-2.4	-4.6	-2.7	0.0	-2.1
-7.1	-4.5	-0.3	6.6	11.0	8.8	-2.3	-3.3	2.8
4.0	2.2	1.2	-5.2	2.7	-1.8	-4.0	6.6	-1.4
5.3	10.0	6.3	15.5	-2.4	6.6	6.3	7.2	5.9
			3.4	6.6	2.0	-3.1	1.1	3.2
-3.6	3.7	23.2	-1.8	9.6	0.9	-1.2	11.1	-6.6
0.0	-2.3	3.3	10.8	5.8	-3.9	14.8	15.6	12.9
3.9	0.7	-0.3	13.6	10.5	—	0.4	14.9	-11.6
10.2	1.7	1.5	—	0.4	-1.5	-5.7	0.1	-5.4
2.5	9.2	8.1	6.6	18.8	-6.0	-0.8	1.8	8.0
			5.3	11.7	-2.3	-4.4	0.4	7.0
4.1	3.1	3.9				-5.5	12.1	5.5
4.5	-7.7	7.0				1.1	6.7	5.9
-5.9	-10.9	-5.4				13.4	14.1	3.9
7.3	0.1	2.7						
8.1	10.2	15.4						
Mean:								
2.8	1.9		5.3		-0.8	0.6	4.0	

* The three blocks of data in this group represent the three sessions run under this condition (see section on procedure).

† Each set of three values throughout the table (e.g., 8.3, 4.3, —7.2) represents a 3-person group.

— Incomplete data.

In the *monadic* case, both roles increased in GSP despite the fact that one was reinforced and the other was not. Yet the trend is in the same direction as in the *dyadic* condition, with the larger increase in the reinforced role. The average increase in GSP for the *monadic* non-reinforced role may result because 20 out of the 30 subjects in this role had previously been in a rewarded role. The fact that two subjects were performing the same role may also have been important. These interpretations will be discussed later.

The high-response role in the *natural* leadership condition and the non-reinforced role in the *dyadic* condition are similar in that they are both unique roles for their groups. The slight increase in GSP (0.6 mV) for the high-response, *natural* leadership role may be attributed to partial reinforcement. The low-response role may be used as a control for the dual non-reinforced role (*monadic*), since it involves a comparable rate of initiation. The higher $\Delta\bar{x}$ GSP (4.0 mV) found in the low-response role when compared to the non-reinforced role (1.9 mV) can also be attributed to partial reinforcement. Thus, the pairing of a role may be related to an increase in GSP level. The low-response subjects were in effect both serving comparable "follower" roles.

Closer inspection of the *monadic* leadership data reveals the sequential effects of repeated experience. Figure 3 is a graph of the actual $\bar{x}$ GSP values session by session. The figure includes the data for a first individual session, a second group session, and a final group session, these all being randomly reinforced. Every group consists of three subjects, an A, B, C set. The figure shows an average of each subject in successive sessions, specifying the subjects' reinforcement history.

It is noteworthy that the A subjects, who were first to achieve reward, maintained their high levels of activation in subsequent sessions

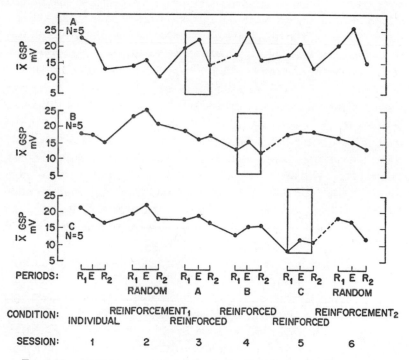

Fig. 3. Mean GSP for successive sessions. R_1 = Initial rest, E = Experiment, R_2 = Final rest.

even though their initiation rate was sharply reduced and they were no longer rewarded.

In contrast, C subjects, who were last to achieve reward, continued to show decreasing levels of physiological activation over time, perhaps suggesting a psychological withdrawal from the continuing experience of failure. Since their behavioral activity was also low during these non-reward sessions, their physiological and behavioral response systems were congruent. When the C subjects were in the reinforced roles (session 5), both GSP and behavior increased together. This finding emphasizes the need to consider the ordering of rewarded experience in understanding psychophysiological relationships.

A dramatic illustration of this ordering effect is found in session 6, in which random reinforcement was used (Fig. 3). Observe the relatively large increase in $\bar{x}$ GSP from resting level to the experimental level for A subjects, as compared with a decrease for both B and C subjects. The A subjects, who were rewarded first, maintained a high level of activation in the task even when their social activity was no longer effective. This level of activation was boosted still further when they were able to initiate activity with some partial reward.

The powerful effects of socially rewarded activity can be seen in the increase in $\bar{x}$ GSP level in the initial rest period of the succeeding session. This increase was established by measuring the difference between the final resting level at the end of a session and the initial resting level of the following session. It was found that a previously rewarded role experience led to an average *increase* of almost 5.0 mV as compared with an average *decrease* of 1.6 mV in the case of non-reward. This difference is statistically significant. Ignoring absolute values, in 11 out of 15 cases for the rewarded role, $\bar{x}$ GSP showed an increase in the following session as compared with only 10 out of 30 for the non-rewarded role ($p = .02$, χ^2 Test).

If we re-examine the difference between the reinforced and non-reinforced roles in the *monadic* leadership condition, confining the comparison to the first *monadic* session (session 3, Fig. 3), we note that the average $\Delta\bar{x}$ GSP for the reinforced role was 2.3 mV (N = 10). Hence, when we consider order of experience, it appears that reward in a role is a crucial variable determining physiological change. These data suggest that the pairing of a role does not necessarily stimulate higher levels of physiological activation, unless the role is at least partially rewarded, as in the *natural* and *dyadic* conditions.

Behavioral-Physiological Interrelationships

The relationship between physiological and behavioral activity within a role was analyzed statistically. Table 3 gives the correlations between $\Delta \bar{x}$ HR, $\Delta \bar{x}$ GSP, and $\bar{x}$ Init. Two results stand out. Changes in $\bar{x}$ GSP were significantly correlated with $\bar{x}$ Init in the *monadic* reinforced role. The more successful the subject was as leader, the greater the increase in GSP. This supports the hypothesis of the relationship between level of arousal and *monadic* leadership. Correlations for the other roles are either negative or zero.

TABLE 3

Rank-Order Correlations Between Initiation Rate and Physiological Change Measures
(Within Session)

Leadership condition	Role	No. of subjects	$\bar{x}$ Init vs $\Delta \bar{x}$ GSP	$\bar{x}$ Init vs $\Delta \bar{x}$ HR	$\bar{x}$ GSP vs $\Delta \bar{x}$ HR
Monadic	Reinforced	15	.53*	.39	.19
	Non-reinforced	30	−.26	−.17	.43*
Dyadic	Reinforced	24	−.26	−.24	−.04
	Non-reinforced	12	−.15	−.37	−.12
Natural	High-response	15	.01	−.02	.32
	Low-response	30	−.11	−.20	.21

Δ = Experimental minus initial rest (algebraic).
* $p < .05$.

The HR variable shows similar trends for the *monadic* leadership role. There is a positive (though not significant) correlation between initiation rate and change in HR, while the other roles have negative or zero correlations. In the *dyadic* condition, the non-reinforced subjects showed an inverse relationship between initiation rate and HR changes. In other words, the more they initiated and were unsuccessful, the more their HR fell. This result suggests, as before, that repeated failure leads to decreased arousal and psychological withdrawal.

The correlations between the two autonomic difference measures are also shown in Table 3. One correlation is significant. In the case of the paired non-reinforced role, the greater the increase in GSP, the less HR decreases. The pattern of these correlations supports the notion that the two autonomic variables should be considered separately. The findings of this study imply that the occasional interrelationship of these variables may depend in part on the social aspects of the situation in which they are measured.

Discussion

We have shown that the roles created for individuals through the manipulation of group decisions can become differentiated. Although individuals may be influenced to initiate activity at varying rates, differences in leadership activity evolve under conditions where total group performance remains relatively constant. Hence, making reinforcement contingent on particular individual social activity leads to changes in the *pattern* of group interaction, but not in the total amount of group activity.

Having established that the social activity of individuals in an interacting group can be differentiated, we asked whether the concomitant autonomic activity of the individuals would also be differentiated. We reasoned that if HR is involved more with regulation of the "milieu intérieur" (Claude Bernard, see Cannon, 1939, p. 38), it should not vary from role to role, at least under conditions of moderate stress and little physical activity. This expectation was confirmed. The contention that HR is a highly stable characteristic of the individual in this social context has also been supported in a physiological study comparing social isolation and social interaction (Shapiro et al., 1964). Heart rate appears to be relatively independent of the particular leadership role the individual takes (at least under conditions of mild stress in this social situation).

On the basis of the social situation-interaction study, we expected that activation level as measured by GSP would be sensitive to variations in the social relationships of the individual. The data support this proposition. The GSP level varies significantly in the different experimentally manipulated roles. One major concept that might explain the obtained results is the reward attained by an individual in leading a group to success. We cannot conclude that reward alone accounts for these results. Rather, it appears that the acts of initiation associated with the leadership role must also be considered.

A second important concept derived from this work is that of coalition formation. A coalition develops between a *pair* of individuals sharing a similar social role. The highest increase in GSP is achieved by those individuals in the paired role that is reinforced, as in the *dyadic* leadership condition. The GSP level rises somewhat less for the *monadic* leaders who, while receiving reinforcement, have no opportunity to form coalitions. When roles are paired without reward (i.e., non-reinforced roles in the *monadic* leadership condition), the findings are less clear. Finally, the subject who neither is rewarded nor has anyone to share this role with him, shows a decrease in activation. The GSP results in the case of natural leadership show a similar ordering for coalition formation. These interpretations of the data are summarized in the following table.

	Role	Leadership condition
1. Task reward—role pairing	Reinforced	Dyadic
2. Task reward—no role pairing	Reinforced	Monadic
3. No task reward—role pairing	Non-reinforced	Monadic
4. No task reward—no role pairing	Non-reinforced	Dyadic
5. Partial task reward—role pairing	Low-response	Natural
6. Partial task reward—no role pairing	High-response	Natural

Processes of pairing and formation of coalitions in a 3-person group have been discussed by Simmel (1950) and by Mills (1960). They claim that coalitions are formed on the basis of solidarity of two persons against a third. Our physiological data are consistent with their formulation, and suggest that when two of the three people share the same role, the activation level of these two individuals is higher than that of the controls. The GSP effects of the coalition formation were found in rewarded roles; however, they were not strikingly present in the partially rewarded roles. We do not know whether the coalitions in our study were formed on a cooperative or a competitive basis. Further work using behavioral methods is required to clarify this problem.

Another intriguing result is the decrease in activation level for the non-successful role when two other persons are being rewarded. While these non-rewarded social isolates did not withdraw behaviorally from group activity, their activation level decreased. Activation level and behavior are no longer congruent, in contrast with the *dyadic* reinforced leadership role, in which they are congruent. If this interpretation can be substantiated, then measurement of GSP level can become a powerful tool in evaluating changes in motivation, independent of the behavioral acts.

Another question raised by the latter findings is whether *social isolation within a group* has a more profound effect on the individual than other types of isolation. On the basis of this study and previous work (Shapiro and Leiderman, 1964), it seems that activation decreases more in social isolation within a group than it does in mere physical isolation. This physiological finding may be unique for 3-person groups, since in larger groups, a subject would have more opportunities to form coalitions.

The influence of the leadership role on the behavioral-physiological relationship is apparent in the findings of this study. Only in the leadership role is the social behavior and physiological activity of the individual in the same direction—that is, both increased. The more initiations, the greater is the increase in GSP, and the smaller is the decrease in HR. Within each of the other roles the correlations are low and negative. The fact that this kind of behavioral-physiological relation does not exist when leadership is shared indicates that there are physiological as well as behavioral differences between the two leadership roles. Additional work on the relationship between behavioral and physiological response systems as well as relationships of autonomic measures to one another under varying types of group composition is needed to clarify these relationships.

A third concept derived from the findings of this study concerns the sequential effects and ordering of successful and unsuccessful experiences. It is known from previous work (Darrow, 1936) that GSR is sensitive to modifications of changes in expectancy. We would make this same interpretation for GSP. We found that the immediately previous experience, if rewarding, led to an increase in resting level of GSP in the subsequent session. An interesting aspect of this finding was the persistence of heightened activation despite subsequent experiences of non-reward. Successive experiences of non-reward, on the other hand, tended to decrease activation. While these results indicate only strong trends, they clearly have implications for the study of expectancy and set under different conditions of social reward and social deprivation.

Summary

We have shown how certain social roles can be experimentally created by the manipulation of success and failure, and have described the consequences of these manipulations for individual social activity and physiological activation within groups. Three major concepts emerged in the analysis of the relationship between acts and activation in a 3-person group: (1) reinforcement of behavior in a leadership role; (2) coalition formation or role sharing; (3) changes in expectancy dependent upon the ordering of success and failure. The techniques and concepts that emerged were shown to be useful for understanding the relationship between social act and physiological activation.

In research as complex as this, the help of several people must not go unnoticed. Of great importance was the technical assistance of Mr. Bernard Tursky, Instrumentation Engineer, and the research assistance of Mrs. Mona Morningstar. We also wish to acknowledge the aid of Kevin Deasy, Catherine Hanley, Anne Horrocks, George Szadis, and David Wolfe.

REFERENCES

Cannon, W. B. *The wisdom of the body.* New York: Norton, 1939.

Darrow, C. W. The galvanic skin reflex (sweating) and blood pressure as preparatory and facilitative functions. *Psychol. Bull.*, 1936, 33, 73–94.

Lacey, J. I., Bateman, Dorothy E., and VanLehn, Ruth. Autonomic response specificity, an experimental study. *Psychosom. Med.*, 1953, 15, 8–21.

Leiderman, P. H., and Shapiro, D. A physiological and behavioral approach to the study of group interaction. *Psychosom. Med.*, 1963, 25, 146–57.

Leiderman, P. H., and Shapiro, D. Studies on galvanic skin potential level: some behavioral correlates. *J. psychosom. Res.*, 1964, 7, 277–81.

Malmo, R. B. Activation. In A. J. Bachrach (Ed.), *Experimental foundations of clinical psychology.* New York: Basic Books, 1962. Pp. 386–422.

Mandler, G., Mandler, Jean M., Kremen, I., and Sholiton, R. D. The response to threat: relations among verbal and physiological indices. *Psychol. Monogr.*, 1961, 75, 1–22.

Mills, T. M. Power relations in three-person groups. In D. Cartwright and A. Zander (Eds.), *Group dynamics*. (2d ed.) Evanston, Ill.: Row, Peterson, 1960. Pp. 766–80.

Morningstar, Mona E. A study of some relationships between reinforcement and physiological responses. Master's thesis, Northeastern University, May, 1963.

Shapiro, D., and Leiderman. P. H. Studies on galvanic skin potential: some statistical properties. *J. psychosom. Res.*, 1964, **7**, 269–75.

Shapiro, D., Leiderman, P. H., and Morningstar, Mona E. Social isolation and social interaction: a behavioral and physiological comparison. In J. Wortis, (Ed.), *Recent advances in biological psychiatry*, Vol. 6. New York: Plenum Press, 1964. Pp. 129–38.

Simmel, G. *The sociology of Georg Simmel*. (Trans. by K. H. Wolff.) Glencoe, Ill.: Free Press, 1950.

Woodworth, R. S., and Schlosberg, H. *Experimental psychology*. New York: Holt, 1954.

A Proposed Program of Research in Sociopharmacology

HENRY L. LENNARD, *Bureau of Applied Social Research,*
Columbia University

Psychotropic drugs have been used extensively in psychiatry and medicine for more than ten years. During this year alone, millions of prescriptions will be written for the group of drugs popularly known as "tranquilizers" and "energizers." They will be prescribed for patients in mental hospitals, and for patients who have returned to their communities from such hospitals. In addition, these drugs will be used for psychiatric and medical conditions ranging from psychoses and severe psychoneuroses to unspecific gastro-intestinal disorders. Most frequently they will be taken for "problems of everyday living," sometimes without the specific recommendation or advice of a physician.

The following comparison illustrates the magnitude of this development: the number of people who have undergone psychotherapy between 1900 and 1940 may well be less than the number of people in the United States whose behavior has been subjected to chemical modification in a single year. Surprisingly, in the light of this significant revolution in the modes of influencing human behavior, very few sociologists are engaged in research on the relationship between drug effect and social processes.

The pharmacologist and the experimental psychiatrist, on the one hand, and the sociologist on the other, have much to learn from each other. Development of theory as well as research on drug effect and social process will have both practical and theoretical consequences for clinical psychiatry, pharmacology, and sociology. The purpose of

The preparation of this paper was supported in part by a Public Health Service Research Career Program Award (MH-K3-18697).

this paper is to demonstrate the fruitfulness of the collaboration by formulating a program for the empirical and theoretical work that needs to be undertaken. Such a statement of the dimensions of the task will hopefully direct attention to the challenges and opportunities of working in "sociopharmacology."

The Identification of the Effects of Drugs Upon Communication Processes

The study of the effects of mental-action drugs is increasing. The techniques used in evaluating these effects are generally rating scales, adjective check lists, and Q sorts. The subjects studied most frequently are hospitalized patients and "normal" volunteers.* A few systematic attempts have been made to specify the effects of drugs upon ongoing interaction processes. These few attempts have focused on the effect of drugs upon communication in experimentally constituted problem-solving groups. A great number of variables still require exploration; for example, patterns of activity and participation under the influence of a variety of drugs should be compared. Several questions could be raised: Which drugs increase or decrease self-initiated or intrusive behavior? Which drugs increase or decrease agreement or disagreement in group interaction? Which drugs facilitate or impede continuity and responsiveness in communication? In a study dealing with this question, H. Lennard, M. E. Jarvik, and H. A. Abramson (1956) found that subjects under the influence of 50 to 100 micrograms of LSD-25, engaged in a discussion on a suggested topic, asked considerably more questions, gave more orientation responses, and disagreed less than when they were in the placebo condition. However, it cannot be assumed that a drug will affect communication in a natural unit, such as a family, in the same way that it will affect communication in an experimentally constituted group operating under the same task conditions. To assess the effects of drugs in differing situations one needs information on the effect of drugs on communication patterns.†

* For a review of methods used in the assessment of drug effect see Uhr and Miller (1960), especially chaps. 43 (Maurice Lorr) and 46 (Vincent Nowlis).
† Progress in developing computer methods as described recently by R. F. Bales (paper on "Progress in Methods of Content Analysis," Eastern Sociological Society, April, 1963), should facilitate the processing of the considerable quantities of verbatim communication data which will need to be collected in studies of effects of drugs on the communication process.

What has been discussed so far is the effect of drugs on communication in relatively short segments of interaction, such as a group problem-solving session, a therapy hour, or an interview. One must be equally concerned to assess the effects of drugs taken over longer periods of time, on more extended and enduring forms of interaction. For example, do individuals under the influence of drugs find it easier or more difficult to form friendships? Do relationships in which some member is taking drugs show characteristic changes over time, such as an increase in closeness and in self-revelation?*

The sociologist may also wish to analyze communication in terms of teaching and learning role requirements, because it has been claimed frequently that some mental-action drugs facilitate learning and performance in the patient role (Rickels, 1963). Little attention, however, has been paid to the quality of role-teaching undertaken by persons under drugs. Yet the teaching of reciprocal role obligations is an essential task performed by parents, teachers, employers, and many others. Table 1 shows some of the areas in which studies of the effects of drugs on social interaction might be undertaken.

TABLE 1

Areas for the Sociological Study of Drug Effects

Effects on dimensions of communication ——→	Effects on patterning of relationships
Rate and volume of communication (e.g., tempo, volume of activity, extent of autonomous and self-initiated activity)	Effects upon system formation (e.g., making friends, entering new situations)
Type of communications (e.g., communications about self, other persons, non-human world, feelings, etc.)	Effects upon maintenance of relationships (e.g., keeping friends, staying married)
Characteristics of sequences of communication (e.g., agreement-disagreement, intrusion, responsiveness)	Effects upon unfolding of relationships (e.g., progression in self-revelation, intimacy)

Social System Attributes and the Effect of Drugs

Experimental psychiatrists and pharmacologists, working on the effects of drugs on animals, have observed that characteristics of the social situation in which a drug is administered influence the effects

* Unfortunately, there is little base-line data available on characteristic changes in social relationships over time, which makes it difficult to evaluate deviations, if there are any, from such patterns.

of drugs on animals. For example, Masserman (1958) points out that the number of animals in the experimental group, their familiarity or lack of familiarity with each other, and characteristics of the task, are variables to be considered. Similarly, characteristics of human social systems may affect an individual's drug response. The following attributes of human social systems may be significant: the size of the group, its age and sex composition, its permanence or impermanence, the purpose for which the group comes together, such as work or play, and the complexity of the task.

TABLE 2

System Attributes and Drug Effect

Attribute	May result in
Size of group	Facilitation or potentiation
Age and sex composition	Blocking of effect
Task or no task	Requirement of change of
Complexity of task	dosage
Experimental, investigative	
Therapeutic situation	

The following example shows how group size might modify the intensity of drug effect. Suppose that group members are given a stimulant drug, such as amphetamine; presumably, the psychomotor activity of group members will increase. The greater the number of individuals in the group, the more the increased activity level and excitability of each member will enhance the action of the drug in the other group members.* The action of the drug and social stimulation both result in increased sympathetic nervous system activity. When the drugs and the social processes affect the same structures, potentiation results. If the social system and the drug affected antagonistic systems, drug response might be decreased. This suggests that group attributes, such as size, and the kinds of interactions flowing from such attributes, can either enhance or decrease the pharmacological action of a group of drugs. Table 2 lists the various system attributes and the effects they may have on the action of the drugs.

Two additional illustrations focus attention on the relationship between characteristics and requirements of social systems and the effects attributed to currently used drugs.

---

* Here a curvilinear relationship may obtain. An excess of stimulation may, in intact subjects, lead to an activation of defenses of withdrawal from stimulation and thus from the group.

Illustration 1.

Social systems tend toward stability in volume and rate of interaction by system members. If an individual member of a group increases or decreases his participation levels beyond set limits, mechanisms are set into motion to adjust his volume and rate of participation.

In a current study on family interaction in families with a schizophrenic child,* I found not only a dearth of communications directed by the child to the father, but a low rate of initiation and entry into father-mother communication by the child. This pattern may be attributed to the parents' discouraging such self-initiated communication by the patient. When such a patient returns to his family environment from the hospital, receiving a drug whose pharmacological action is intended to increase sensory-motor activity, disruption of the familial interaction patterns can be expected. In the hospital the patient may be able to vary his activity and participation patterns considerably. His return home brings the pharmacological action of the drug on increased activity and initiative into conflict with the constraints on the patient's behavior imposed by his family. The question raised is, are the forces tending toward behavior equilibrium in the family strong enough to restrict the patient to his pre-hospital mode of activity despite pharmacological influences?

The interaction of drug and behavior may be greater when an individual is part of a new social system, where a greater repertoire of behavior is permitted. An increase or decrease in certain behaviors would then not tend to violate previously established norms. This implies that the effect of an activity-increasing agent administered to a schizophrenic child might be different if the child were to live with a foster family rather than with his own. In this case the new family system might support different levels of self-initiated activity on the part of the child.

Illustration 2.

Most social systems require minimum levels of behavior from their members, though systems vary in the amount and type of social exchange between the members. Three requirements have been estab-

* This reference is to a study comparing interaction patterns in ten families with a child diagnosed as "schizophrenic" with interaction patterns in a group of "control" families, carried out at the Bureau of Applied Social Research at Columbia University by Henry L. Lennard.

lished by sociologists: (a) system members must show some awareness of each other's actions and reactions, some responsiveness toward
each other; (b) systems must maintain some minimum level of cognitive input; (c) systems must maintain a minimum level of affective
or emotional input. The effect of some psychotropic drugs has been
hypothesized as modifying perceptual input. Consider the requirements of a mother-child relationship: the mother, discharged from
the hospital, is under the effects of a phenothiazine drug, such as
Thorazine. Her responsiveness, her potential for receiving and supplying cognitive and emotional communications, is reduced. Nevertheless, she is required to function in a mother-child relationship and to
provide cognitive and emotional communications. A sociological perspective suggests the hypothesis that what is functional for the mother's maintenance of psychic functioning may be dysfunctional for the
mother-child sub-system. Thus, while chemically reducing the severity
of behavior disorder in the mother, the drug may increase difficulties
in the mother-child relationship.

It has been suggested* that one result of the mother's dearth of responsiveness might be, paradoxically, an increase in the amount of
stimulation directed to her by the child. Assuming that other aspects
of the interaction remain the same, the increased number of stimuli
from the child would return the number of stimuli received by the
mother to the pre-drug level. Thus, hypothetically, homeostatic social
processes may operate to decrease the individual's observable response to the drug.

Psychiatrists vary the dosage of a drug according to the social situation in which their patients live. Some psychiatrists increase the dosage of an anti-depressant drug for patients returning from the hospital to their family setting, and lower the dosage of activity-decreasing
drugs for other patients under similar circumstances. A dosage of
Thorazine administered to patients who are living with their families
can produce unsatisfactory results, while slightly higher dosages of
the same drug administered to hospitalized patients can yield most
satisfactory results.

As a consequence of increased utilization of drugs, many hospitalized patients have returned to their families and communities. In

* Donald Meyers, M.D., personal communication.

continuing therapy with such patients, psychiatrists must consider the social situation to which they have returned, and evaluate the consequences of drug effect on social behavior. This clinical problem raises several issues for the behavioral scientist. What are the consequences of such chemical manipulation of human behavior under conditions of incomplete information about social process? What are the secondary effects of influencing one member of a social system in this fashion? Just as the exploration of drug effect on particular physiological systems is not possible without the study of these systems, so judgments of the severity or toxicity of secondary drug effects must include the study of behavioral processes in the social system in which the individual operates. Table 3 lists some possible results of the interaction between system requirements and drug effects.

TABLE 3

System Processes and Drug Effect

System requirements	plus	May result in
Tendency toward stability in volume and rate of communication	Physio-logical action of drugs	Increase in constraints on behavior affected by drugs
Minimal cognitive and affective levels		Drug action in groups the reverse of that seen in individuals
Differentiation of action over time		Homeostatic processes that decrease drug action

Effects of Attitudinal and Expectational Processes

The influence of expectations, beliefs, definitions of the situation on drug action, and the reporting of such experiences, has been frequently emphasized. Particularly the placebo response has been widely studied. In a recent conference on LSD-25, it was reported that differences in LSD effect varied with the situation in which the drug was given, whether investigative, experimental, or therapeutic. Patients who received LSD-25 in an investigative setting reported disliking the effects of the drug,* while patients receiving the drug in a situation defined as therapeutic expressed a desire for repeated

---

* "We were studying the drug, not giving it therapeutically. The majority of our patients, with very rare exceptions, did not enjoy the experience and did not want to go through it again, ever." (S. Malitz, in Lennard and Hewitt, 1960, p. 213.)

administration. Seymour Fisher's (1963) research suggests that "the therapeutic attitude potentiates only drug but not placebo effects, while the experimental attitude interacts negatively with both drug and placebo conditions."

The significance of expectation and attitude has been documented for many drugs, especially pain-relieving drugs. For example, "Attitudes towards a wound determine the need for the drug. . . . Thus, soldiers to whom a wound can be a symbol of survival (rather than evidence of injury) require less morphine than civilian post-operative patients, to whom (despite far less tissue damage) the operation may signify severe disability" (Beecher, 1962, p. 63).

Such observations clearly indicate the need to determine what individuals expect from a drug. Do they expect different performances from themselves when taking the drug? Do they expect others to react and treat them differently? The expectations of the role partners of persons who are taking drugs are equally significant. A hypothesis often advanced is that favorable prognoses for mental patients are attributable in part to changes in the social perception of patients resulting from the widespread use of mental action drugs. These changes consist in revised expectations by hospital personnel of patients taking drugs, and the resulting modifications of the personnel's behavior which eventually produce changes in the patient. Acceptance of former mental patients by the community may involve a similar cycle.* Table 4 lists some of the expectations of or attitudes toward taking the drug and some of the influences these may have on the effects of the drug.

TABLE 4

Influence of Expectations and Attitudes on Drug Effect

Expectation or attitude	May influence
Expectation of relief	Degree of relief of symptoms
Expectation of feelings or ideas to be generated	Types of content produced
	Dosage required
Expectation of behavioral change	Desire for drug
Attitude toward illness for which drug is given	

* Schwartz, M., in Lecture delivered before Seminar in Sociology of Mental Health, Columbia University, April 2, 1963.

Drug Selection to Meet System Requirements

In the past, pharmacologists have concerned themselves with the development of drugs, leaving others to assess the effect of these drugs on social systems. It might be fruitful for sociologists to ask pharmacologists to devise agents to affect specific operations of social systems. For instance, the sociologist might ask which drug, when administered to husband or wife, might make for more consensus and complementarity in marriage; he might ask which drugs enable a mother to socialize her child more effectively into its respective age and sex roles. Are there drugs which will facilitate more accurate discrimination between modes of communication, especially incongruent modes? With regard to the last question some suggestions were provided by interview data on hospitalized schizophrenic patients (Lennard and Hewitt, 1960) who had been administered LSD-25 over a period of days. During the later sessions patients talked more freely about conflicting parental communications. This suggests that LSD conceivably facilitates discrimination of incongruent modes of communication. Thus, the target of drug research need be not only relief of psychological disturbances and symptoms, but reduction of social system strains and improvement of social system functioning.

The Use of Drugs in an Experimental Sociology

The use of mental-action drugs introduces new possibilities for experimental research in sociology. Sociologists can now clarify the mechanisms of homeostatic social systems by experimental techniques. For example, drugs that impair functioning of the individual enable the sociologist to observe the modifications of group performance of a given task. In the research on LSD, the ratio of instrumental to expressive acts (Bales coding) was surprisingly similar for a group of four subjects in the LSD-25 and placebo conditions. Although the literature on LSD (Rinkel et al., 1955) reports that the drug increases hostility, irritability, and suspicious behavior, our group of subjects, engaged in a discussion task, manifested less disagreement and expression of antagonism under LSD-25 than in the placebo condition. This finding contributes to an understanding of interaction processes under conditions of individual impairment. The experimental group under LSD differed from the placebo group in showing an increase in communications giving and requesting orientation, an increase in solidarity and tension release, and a decrease in disagreement and antagonism. This preliminary result suggests the hypothesis that groups operating under a task condition will cope with drug impairments in individual members by supplying information, searching for cues, and providing emotional solidarity.

Epidemiology of Drug Use

I have estimated earlier that perhaps the numerically largest group of persons taking "tranquilizers" or "energizers" do so to meet "problems of everyday living." Although information about the prevalence of drug use can be obtained for psychiatric and medical practice in institutional settings, special studies are required to determine the epidemiology of therapeutic drug use in the general population. Studies might address themselves to the location in the social structure of individuals who want to modify their performances through drugs. In which occupations or industries are they found? In which positions within organizations are they probably located?

Studies of Social Behavioral Toxicity

Classical pharmacological techniques did not provide the means for studying the effects of drugs on individual and social behavior. The development of psychopharmacology permitted the study of drug effect on psychological functions and individual behavior. Attention must now be directed to the evaluation of drug action on interpersonal behavior systems and processes. Like the unanticipated effects of thalidomide on fetal development, there may be drug effects on specific behavioral systems that are currently being ignored. For example, there may be untoward effects of tranquilizing drugs on "parenting" and family functions. There is the likelihood that new psychiatric syndromes may become apparent in children raised by parents who have been under chronic drug administration. This type of phenomenon demands not only new screening methods for drugs but attention to naturalistic studies of families who are currently and have in the past used pharmacological agents.

Concluding Note

This paper briefly delineates seven research areas in which collaboration between the sociologist, the pharmacologist, and the psychiatrist should prove fruitful. First, it describes the need for more research in the effect of mental-action drugs upon specific patterns of communication between individuals. Second, the paper indicates characteristics of social systems that may limit or alter the effectiveness of a drug. Third, the significance of attitudes and expectations in relation to drug effect is reiterated. Fourth, a focus on behavioral targets is advocated for the pharmacologist. Fifth, drug-induced behavior modification is seen as opening new avenues for experimental sociological research. Sixth, the need for more information in identifying "users" of mental-action drugs is stressed. Seventh, the possibility of undesirable and unanticipated consequences of the widespread use of mental-action drugs within "natural" social systems is mentioned. All of the research questions posed here will require extensive investigation during the next decade.

REFERENCES

Beecher, H. K. Quoted in J. Elkes (Ed.), *Subjective and objective observations in psychiatry.* Harvey Lectures. New York: Academic Press, 1962.

Fisher, Seymour. Quoted in K. Rickels, Psychopharmacologic agents: a clinical psychiatrist's individualistic point of view: patient and doctor variable. *J. nerv. Dis.*, 1963, 136, 540–49.

Lennard, Henry L., and Hewitt, Mollie P. The study of communication processes under LSD. In H. A. Abramson (Ed.), *The use of LSD in psychotherapy.* The Josiah Macy, Jr., Foundation, 1960. Pp. 199–240.

Lennard, H., Jarvik, M. E., and Abramson, H. A. Lysergic acid diethylamide (LSD-25): XII. a preliminary statement of its effects upon interpersonal communication. *J. Psychol.*, 1956, 41, 185–98.

Masserman, J. H. Experimental psychopharmacology and behavioral relativity. In P. Hoch and J. Zubin (Eds.), *Problems of addiction and habituation.* New York: Grune and Stratton, 1958.

Rickels, J. The use of psychotherapy with drugs in the treatment of anxiety. Paper presented at Symposium on Anxiety and Depression, Atlantic City, June 1963.

Rinkel, M., Hyde, R. W., Solomon, H. C., and Hoagland, H. Experimental psychiatry. Clinical and physio-chemical observations in experimental psychosis. *Amer. J. Psychiat.*, 1955, 11, 881–85.

Uhr, L., and Miller, J. S. (Eds.). *Drugs and behavior.* New York: Wiley, 1960.

The Interaction of Cognitive and Physiological Determinants of Emotional State

STANLEY SCHACHTER, *Columbia University*

Many years ago, piqued by the disorderly cataloguing of symptoms that characterized the then classic works on emotion, William James offered what was probably the first simple, integrating, theoretical statement on the nature of emotion. This well-known formulation stated simply that "the bodily changes follow directly the perception of the exciting fact, and that our feeling of the same changes as they occur *is* the emotion." (James, 1890, p. 449.) Since James's proposition equates bodily changes and visceral feelings with emotion, it must follow first, that the different emotions will be accompanied by recognizably different bodily states, and second, that the manipulation of bodily state, by drugs or surgery, will also manipulate emotional state. These implications have, directly or indirectly, guided much of the research on emotion since James's day. The results of this research, on the whole, provided little support for a purely visceral formulation of emotion, and led Cannon (1927, 1929) to his brilliant and devastating critique of the James-Lange theory—a critique based on these points:

1. The total separation of the viscera from the central nervous system does not alter emotional behavior.

2. The same visceral changes occur in very different emotional states and in non-emotional states.

3. The viscera are relatively insensitive structures.

Much of the research described in this paper was supported by Grant MH 05203 from the National Institute of Mental Health, United States Public Health Service, and by Grant G 23758 from the National Science Foundation.

4. Visceral changes are too slow to be a source of emotional feeling.

5. The artificial induction of visceral changes that are typical of strong emotions does not produce the emotions.

Though new data have weakened the cogency of some of these points, on the whole Cannon's logic and findings make it inescapably clear that a completely peripheral or visceral formulation of emotion, such as the James-Lange theory, is simply inadequate to cope with the facts. In an effort to deal with the obvious inadequacies of a purely visceral or peripheral formulation of emotion, Ruckmick (1936), Hunt, Cole, and Reis (1958), Schachter (1959), and others have suggested that cognitive factors may be major determinants of emotional states. In this paper I shall attempt to spell out the implications of a cognitive-physiological formulation of emotion and to describe a series of experiments designed to test these implications.

To begin, let us grant, on the basis of much evidence (see Woodworth and Schlosberg, 1954, for example), that a general pattern of sympathetic discharge is characteristic of emotional states. Given such a state of arousal, it is suggested that one labels, interprets, and identifies this state in terms of the characteristics of the precipitating situation and one's apperceptive mass. This suggests, then, that an emotional state may be considered a function of a state of physiological arousal* and a cognition appropriate to this state of arousal. The cognition, in a sense, exerts a steering function. Cognitions arising from the immediate situation as interpreted by past experience provide the framework within which one understands and labels one's feelings. It is the cognition that determines whether the state of physiological arousal will be labeled "anger," "joy," or whatever.

In order to examine the implications of this formulation let us consider how these two elements—a state of physiological arousal and cognitive factors—would interact in a variety of situations. In most emotion-inducing situations, of course, the two factors are com-

---

* Though the experiments to be described are concerned largely with the physiological changes produced by the injection of adrenalin, which appear to be primarily the result of sympathetic excitation, the term physiological arousal is used in preference to the more specific "excitement of the sympathetic nervous system" because there are indications, to be discussed later, that this formulation is applicable to a variety of bodily states.

pletely interrelated. Imagine a man walking alone down a dark alley when a figure with a gun suddenly appears. The perception-cognition "figure with a gun" in some fashion initiates a state of physiological arousal; this state of arousal is interpreted in terms of knowledge about dark alleys and guns, and the state of arousal is labeled "fear." Similarly, a student who unexpectedly learns that he has made Phi Beta Kappa may experience a state of arousal which he will label "joy."

Let us now consider circumstances in which these two elements, the physiological and the cognitive, are, to some extent, independent. First, is the state of physiological arousal alone sufficient to induce an emotion? Best evidence indicates that it is not. Marañon (1924), in a fascinating study (which was replicated by Cantril and Hunt (1932) and Landis and Hunt (1932)), injected 210 of his patients with the sympathomimetic agent adrenalin and then asked them to introspect. Seventy-one per cent of his subjects simply reported physical symptoms with no emotional overtone; 29 per cent of the subjects responded in an apparently emotional fashion. Of these, the great majority described their feelings in a way that Marañon labeled "cold" or "as if" emotions; that is, they made statements such as "I feel *as if* I were afraid" or "*as if* I were awaiting a great happiness." This is a sort of emotional "déjà vu" experience; these subjects are neither happy nor afraid, but only feel "as if" they were. Finally, a very few cases apparently reported a genuine emotional experience. However, in order to produce this reaction in most of these few cases, Marañon points out, "one must suggest a memory with strong affective force but not so strong as to produce an emotion in the normal state. For example, before the injection, in several cases, we spoke to our patients about their sick children or dead parents, and they responded calmly to this topic. The same topic presented later, during the adrenal commotion, was sufficient to trigger emotion. This adrenal commotion places the subject in a situation of 'affective imminence.' " Apparently, then, to produce a genuinely emotional reaction to adrenalin, Marañon was forced to provide such subjects with an appropriate cognition.

Though Marañon does not explicitly describe his procedure, it is clear that his subjects knew that they were receiving an injection, and in all likelihood they knew that they were receiving adrenalin and probably had some familiarity with its effects. In short, though they underwent the pattern of sympathetic discharge common to strong emotional states, at the same time they had a completely appropriate cognition or explanation of why they felt this way. This, I would suggest, is the reason so few of Marañon's subjects reported any emotional experience.

Consider next a person in a state of physiological arousal for which no immediately explanatory or appropriate cognitions are available. Such a state could result were one to inject a subject with adrenalin covertly, or, unknown to him, to feed the subject a sympathomimetic drug such as ephedrine. Under such conditions a subject would be aware of palpitations, tremor, face flushing, and most of the symptoms associated with a discharge of the sympathetic nervous system. In contrast to Marañon's subjects, he would be utterly unaware of why he felt this way. What would be the consequence of such a state?

Schachter (1959) has suggested that just such a state would lead to the arousal of "evaluative needs" (Festinger, 1954); that is, an individual in this state would feel pressures to understand and label his bodily feelings. His bodily state grossly resembles the condition in which it has been at times of emotional excitement. How would he label his present feelings? It is suggested, of course, that he will label his feelings in terms of his knowledge of the immediate situation.* Should he at the time be with a beautiful woman he might decide that he was wildly in love or sexually excited. Should he be at a gay party, he might, by comparing himself to others, decide that he was extremely happy and euphoric. Should he be arguing with his wife, he might explode in fury and hatred. Or, should the situation be completely inappropriate, he might decide that he was excited about something that had recently happened to him, or, simply, that he was sick. In any case, it is my basic assumption that emotional states are a function of the interaction of such cognitive factors with a state of physiological arousal.

* This suggestion is not new. Several psychologists have suggested that situational factors should be considered the chief differentiators of the emotions. Hunt, Cole, and Reis (1958) probably make this point most explicitly in their study distinguishing among fear, anger, and sorrow in terms of situational characteristics.

This line of thought, then, leads to the following propositions:

1. Given a state of physiological arousal for which an individual has no immediate explanation, he will "label" this state and describe his feelings in terms of the cognitions available to him. To the extent that cognitive factors are potent determiners of emotional states, one might anticipate that precisely the same state of physiological arousal could be labeled "joy" or "fury" or any of a great number of emotional labels, depending on the cognitive aspects of the situation.

2. Given a state of physiological arousal for which an individual has a completely appropriate explanation (e.g., "I feel this way because I have just received an injection of adrenalin"), no evaluative needs will arise and the individual is unlikely to label his feelings in terms of the alternative cognitions available.

Finally, consider a condition in which emotion-inducing cognitions are present but there is no state of physiological arousal. For example, an individual might be completely aware that he is in great danger but for some reason (drug or surgical) might remain in a state of physiological quiescence. Does he experience the emotion "fear"? This formulation of emotion as a joint function of a state of physiological arousal and an appropriate cognition, would, of course, suggest that he does not, which leads to my final proposition.

3. Given the same cognitive circumstances, the individual will react emotionally or describe his feelings as emotions only to the extent that he experiences a state of physiological arousal.*

The Experiments

The experimental test of these propositions requires (1) the experimental manipulation of a state of physiological arousal or sympathetic activation; (2) the manipulation of the extent to which the subject has an appropriate or proper explanation of his bodily state; and (3) the creation of situations from which explanatory cognitions may be derived.

---

* In his critique of the James-Lange theory of emotion, Cannon (1929) makes the point that sympathectomized animals and patients do seem to manifest emotional behavior. This criticism is, of course, as applicable to the above proposition as it was to the James-Lange formulation. The issues involved will be discussed later in this chapter.

In order to satisfy these experimental requirements, Schachter and Singer (1962) designed an experiment that was cast in the framework of a study of the effects of vitamin supplements on vision. As soon as a subject arrived, he was taken to a private room and told by the experimenter:

In this experiment we would like to make various tests of your vision. We are particularly interested in how certain vitamin compounds and vitamin supplements affect the visual skills. In particular, we want to find out how the vitamin compound called "Suproxin" affects your vision.

What we would like to do, then, if we can get your permission, is to give you a small injection of Suproxin. The injection itself is mild and harmless; however, since some people do object to being injected we don't want to talk you into anything. Would you mind receiving a Suproxin injection?

If the subject agreed to the injection (and all but one of 185 subjects did), the experimenter continued with instructions we shall describe below, and then left the room. In a few minutes a doctor (a genuine M.D.) entered the room, briefly repeated the experimenter's instructions, took the subject's pulse, and then injected him with Suproxin.

Depending upon the experimental condition, the subject received one of two forms of Suproxin—epinephrine or a placebo.

Epinephrine or adrenalin is a sympathomimetic drug whose effects, with minor exceptions, are almost a perfect mimicry of a discharge of the sympathetic nervous system. Shortly after injection, systolic blood pressure increases markedly, heart rate increases somewhat, cutaneous blood flow decreases while muscular and cerebral blood flow increase, blood sugar and lactic acid concentrations increase, and respiration rate increases slightly. The major subjective symptoms noted by the subject are palpitation, tremor, and sometimes a feeling of flushing and accelerated breathing. With a subcutaneous injection (in the dosage administered to our subjects) these effects usually begin within 3 to 5 minutes of injection and last anywhere from 10 minutes to an hour. For most subjects the effects are dissipated within 15 to 20 minutes after injection.

Subjects receiving epinephrine received a subcutaneous injection of ½ cc of a 1:1000 solution of Winthrop Laboratories' Suprarenin, a saline solution of epinephrine bitartrate. Subjects in the placebo condition received a subcutaneous injection of ½ cc of saline solution.

Manipulating an Appropriate Explanation

By "appropriate" I refer to the extent to which the subject has an authoritative, unequivocal explanation of his bodily condition. Thus, a subject who had been informed by the physician that as a direct consequence of the injection he would feel palpitations, tremor, and so on would be considered to have a completely appropriate explanation. A subject who had been informed only that the injection would have no side effects would have no appropriate explanation of his state. This dimension of appropriateness was manipulated in three experimental conditions, which shall be called:

1. Epinephrine Informed (Epi Inf),
2. Epinephrine Ignorant (Epi Ign),
3. Epinephrine Misinformed (Epi Mis).

Immediately after the subject had agreed to the injection and before the physician entered the room, the experimenter gave one of the following speeches, depending on the condition:

1. *Epinephrine Informed.*

I should also tell you that some of our subjects have experienced side effects from the Suproxin. These side effects are transitory; that is, they will last only for about 15 or 20 minutes. What will probably happen is that your hand will start to shake, your heart will start to pound, and your face may get warm and flushed. Again, these are side effects lasting 15 or 20 minutes.

While the physician was giving the injection, she told the subject that the injection was mild and harmless, and repeated the description of the symptoms that the subject could expect as a consequence of the injection. In this condition, then, subjects have a completely appropriate explanation of their bodily state. They know precisely what they will feel and why.

2. *Epinephrine Ignorant.* In this condition, when the subject agreed to the injection, the experimenter said nothing more about side effects and simply left the room. While the physician was giving the injection, she told the subject that the injection was mild and harmless and would have no side effects. In this condition, then, the subject has no experimentally provided explanation for his bodily state.

3. *Epinephrine Misinformed.*

I should also tell you that some of our subjects have experienced side effects from the Suproxin. These side effects are transitory, that is, they will last only for about 15 or 20 minutes. What will probably happen is that your feet will feel numb, you will have an itching sensation over parts of your body, and you may get a slight headache. Again, these are side effects lasting 15 or 20 minutes.

And again, the physician repeated these symptoms while injecting the subject.

None of these symptoms, of course, are consequences of an injection of epinephrine and, in effect, these instructions provide the subject with a completely inappropriate explanation of his bodily feelings. This condition was introduced as a control condition of sorts. It seemed possible that the description of side effects in the Epi Inf condition might make the subject introspective and possibly slightly troubled. Differences in the dependent variable between the Epi Inf and Epi Ign conditions might, then, be due to such factors rather than to differences in appropriateness. The false symptoms in the Epi Mis condition should similarly make the subject introspective, but the instructions in this condition do not provide an appropriate explanation of the subject's state.

Subjects in all of the above conditions were injected with epinephrine. Finally, there was a placebo condition, in which subjects were injected with saline solution and were then given precisely the same treatment as subjects in the Epi Ign condition.

Producing an Emotion-Inducing Cognition

My initial hypothesis suggested that given a state of physiological arousal for which the individual has no adequate explanation, cognitive factors can lead the individual to describe his feelings with any of a number of emotional labels. In order to test this hypothesis, it was decided to manipulate two emotional states that can be considered quite different—euphoria and anger.

There are, of course, many ways to induce such states. In my own program of research, we have concentrated on social determinants of emotional states. We have demonstrated in other studies that people evaluate their own feelings by comparing themselves with others around them (Wrightsman, 1960; Schachter, 1959). In the experiment being described, an attempt was again made to manipulate emotional state by social means. In one set of conditions, the subject was placed with a stooge who had been trained to act euphorically. In a second set of conditions the subject was placed with a stooge trained to act in an angry fashion.

Euphoria. Immediately* after the subject had been injected, the physician left the room and the experimenter returned with a stooge whom he introduced as another subject. The experimenter then said:

Both of you have had the Suproxin shot and you'll both be taking the same tests of vision. What I ask you to do now is just wait for 20 minutes. The reason for this is simply that we have to allow 20 minutes for the Suproxin to get from the injection site into the bloodstream. At the end of 20 minutes, when we are certain that most of the Suproxin has been absorbed into the bloodstream, we'll begin the tests of vision.

The room in which this was said had been deliberately put into a state of mild disarray. As he was leaving, the experimenter apologetically added, "The only other thing I should do is to apologize for the condition of the room. I just didn't have time to clean it up. So, if you need any scratch paper or rubber bands or pencils, help yourself. I'll be back in 20 minutes to begin the vision tests."

As soon as the experimenter had left, the stooge introduced himself again, made a series of standard icebreaking comments, and then launched his routine:

He reached first for a piece of paper, doodled briefly, crumpled the paper, aimed for a wastebasket, threw, and missed. This led him into a game of "basketball," in which he moved about the room crumpling paper and trying out fancy basketball shots. Finished with basketball, he said, "This is one of my good days. I feel like a kid again. I think I'll make a plane." He made a paper plane, spent a few minutes flying it around the room, and then said, "Even when I was a kid, I was never much good at this." He then tore off the tail of his plane, wadded it up, and making a slingshot of a rubber band, began to shoot the paper. While shooting, he noticed a sloppy pile of manila folders. He built a tower of these folders, then went to the opposite end of the room to shoot at the tower. He knocked down the tower, and while picking up the folders, he noticed behind a portable blackboard a

---

* It was, of course, imperative that the sequence with the stooge begin before the subject felt his first symptoms, since otherwise the subject would be virtually forced to interpret his feelings in terms of events preceding the stooge's entrance. Pretests had indicated that for most subjects, epinephrine-induced symptoms began within 3 to 5 minutes after injection. A deliberate attempt was made then to bring in the stooge within one minute after the subject's injection.

pair of hula hoops. He took one of these for himself, put the other within reaching distance of the subject and began hula hooping. After a few minutes of this he replaced the hula hoop and returned to his seat, at which point the experimenter returned to the room.

All through this madness an observer, through a one-way mirror, systematically recorded the subject's behavior and noted the extent to which the subject joined in the stooge's whirl of activity.

Subjects in each of the three "appropriateness" conditions and in the placebo condition were submitted to this setup. The stooge, of course, never knew in which condition any particular subject fell.

Anger. Immediately after the injection, the experimenter brought a stooge into the subject's room, introduced the two, and after explaining the necessity for a 20-minute delay for "the Suproxin to get from the injection site into the bloodstream," he continued, "We would like you to use these 20 minutes to answer these questionnaires." Then handing out the questionnaires, he concluded, "I'll be back in 20 minutes to pick up the questionnaires and begin the tests of vision."

The questionnaires, five pages long, began innocently, requesting face-sheet information, and then grew increasingly personal and insulting, asking questions such as:

"With how many men (other than your father) has your mother had extra-marital relationships?

4 and under_____; 5–9_____; 10 and over_____."

The stooge, sitting directly opposite the subject, paced his own answers so that at all times subject and stooge were working on the same question. At regular points in the questionnaire, the stooge made standardized comments about the questions. His comments started innocently enough, but grew increasingly querulous. Finally, in a rage, he tore up his questionnaire, slammed it to the floor, saying "I'm not wasting any more time. I'm getting my books and leaving," and stamped out of the room.

Again an observer recorded the subject's behavior.

In summary, this is a 7-condition experiment that for two different emotional states allows us (1) to evaluate the effects of "appropriateness" on emotional inducibility, and (2) to begin to evaluate the effects of sympathetic activation on emotional inducibility. In schematic form the conditions are the following:

Euphoria	*Anger*
Epi Inf	Epi Inf
Epi Ign	Epi Ign
Epi Mis	Placebo
Placebo	

The Epi Mis condition was not run in the anger sequence. This was originally conceived as a control condition and it was felt that its inclusion in the euphoria conditions alone would suffice as a means of evaluating the possible artifactual effect of the Epi Inf instructions.

The subjects were all male college students taking classes in introductory psychology at the University of Minnesota. The records of all potential subjects were reviewed by the Student Health Service in order to ensure that no harmful effects would result from the injections.

Measurement.   Two types of measurements of emotional state were obtained. Standardized observation through a one-way mirror was used to assess the subject's behavior. To what extent did he join in with the stooge's pattern of behavior and act euphoric or angry? The second type was a self-report questionnaire in which, on a variety of scales, the subject indicated his mood of the moment.

These measurements were obtained immediately after the stooge had finished his routine, at which point the experimenter returned, saying:

Before we proceed with the vision tests, there is one other kind of information we must have. We have found that there are many things besides Suproxin that affect how well you see in our tests. How hungry you are, how tired you are, and even the mood you're in at the moment—whether you feel happy or irritated at the time of testing—will affect how well you see. To understand the data we collect on you, then, we must be able to figure out which effects are due to causes such as these and which are caused by Suproxin.

He then handed out questionnaires containing a number of questions about bodily and emotional state. To measure mood, the following two were the crucial questions:

1. How irritated, angry, or annoyed would you say you feel at present?

I don't feel at all irritated or angry	I feel a little irritated and angry	I feel quite irritated and angry	I feel very irritated and angry	I feel extremely irritated and angry
(0)	(1)	(2)	(3)	(4)

2. How good or happy would you say you feel at present?

I don't feel at all happy or good	I feel a little happy and good	I feel quite happy and good	I feel very happy and good	I feel extremely happy and good
(0)	(1)	(2)	(3)	(4)

The Effects of the Manipulations on Emotional State
Euphoria

The effects of the several manipulations on emotional state in the euphoria conditions are presented in Table 1. The scores recorded in this table are derived, for each subject, by subtracting the value of the point he checks on the "irritation" scale from the value of the point he checks on the "happiness" scale. Thus, if a subject were to check the point "I feel a little irritated and angry" on the "irritation" scale, and the point "I feel very happy and good" on the "happiness" scale, his score would be $+2$. The higher the positive value, the happier and better the subject reports himself to be feeling. Though an index is employed for expositional simplicity, it should be noted that each of the two components of the index yields results completely consistent with those obtained by using this index.

TABLE 1

Self-Report of Emotional State in the Euphoria Conditions

Condition	N	Self-report scales
Epi Inf	25	0.98
Epi Ign	25	1.78
Epi Mis	25	1.90
Placebo	26	1.61

Values of p: Epi Inf vs. Epi Mis, $<.01$; Epi Inf vs. Epi Ign, $.02$; placebo vs. Epi Mis, Epi Ign, or Epi Inf, n.s. All p values reported in this paper are two-tailed.

Let us examine first the effects of the "appropriateness" instructions. A comparison of the scores of the Epi Mis and Epi Inf conditions makes it immediately clear that the experimental differences are not due to artifacts resulting from the "informed" instructions. In both conditions the subject was warned to expect a variety of symptoms as a consequence of the injection. In the Epi Mis condition, where the symptoms were inappropriate to the subject's bodily state, the self-report score is almost twice that in the Epi Inf condition, where the symptoms were completely appropriate to the subject's bodily state. It is reasonable, then, to attribute differences between informed subjects and those in other conditions to differences in manipulated appropriateness rather than to artifacts such as introspectiveness.

It is clear that, consistent with expectations, subjects were more susceptible to the stooge's mood, and consequently more euphoric, when they had no explanation of their own bodily states than when they had one. The means of both the Epi Ign and Epi Mis conditions are considerably larger than the mean of the Epi Inf condition.

Comparing the placebo condition to the epinephrine conditions, we note a pattern that will be repeated throughout the data. Placebo subjects are less euphoric than either Epi Mis or Epi Ign subjects, but somewhat more euphoric than Epi Inf subjects. These differences are not, however, statistically significant. I shall consider the epinephrine-placebo comparisons in detail later in this chapter. For the moment, it is clear from these self-reports that manipulating "appropriateness" has had a very strong effect on euphoria.

The analysis of the observational data is reported in detail elsewhere (Schachter and Singer, 1962). Here it is sufficient to note that on all behavioral indices devised—e.g., the amount of time the subject spends on stooge-initiated activity, "creative euphoria" (the extent to which the subject initiates euphoric activities of his own devising)—the same pattern of between-condition relationships holds. Subjects in the Epi Mis and Epi Ign conditions behave more euphorically than subjects in the Epi Inf condition. Placebo subjects again fall between Epi Ign and Epi Inf subjects.

Anger

In the anger conditions we should again expect that the subject will catch the stooge's mood only in those conditions where he has been injected with epinephrine and has no appropriate explanation for the bodily state thus created. Subjects in the Epi Ign condition should, then, be considerably angrier than those in the Epi Inf or the placebo condition. Data on behavioral indications of anger are presented in Table 2. These figures are derived from a coding of the subject's comments and behavior during the experimental session with the angry stooge. The nature of the index devised is described in detail elsewhere (Schachter and Singer, 1962). For present purposes, it is sufficient to note that a positive value of this index indicates that the subject agrees with the stooge's comments and is angry. The larger the positive value, the angrier the subject. A negative value indicates that the subject either disagrees with the stooge or ignores him.

Table 2

Behavioral Indications of Emotional State in the Anger Conditions

Condition	N	Anger index
Epi Inf	22	−0.18
Epi Ign	23	+2.28
Placebo	22	+0.79

Values of p: Epi Inf vs. Epi Ign, <.01; Epi Ign vs. placebo; <.05; placebo vs. Epi Inf, n.s.

It is evident in Table 2 that expectations are confirmed. The value for the Epi Ign condition is positive and large, indicating that the subjects have become angry, whereas in the Epi Inf condition the score is slightly negative, indicating that these subjects have completely failed to catch the stooge's mood. Placebo subjects fall between Epi Ign and Epi Inf subjects. On the self-report scales of mood, this pattern is repeated, though on this measure, placebo subjects do not differ significantly from either Epi Ign or Epi Inf subjects.

Now that the basic data of this study have been presented, let us examine closely how well they conform to theoretical expectations. If my hypotheses are correct and if this experimental design provided a perfect test for these hypotheses, it should be anticipated that in the euphoria conditions the degree of experimentally produced euphoria should vary in the following way:

$$\text{Epi Mis} \geqq \text{Epi Ign} > \text{Epi Inf} = \text{placebo} .$$

And in the anger conditions, anger should conform to the following pattern:

$$\text{Epi Ign} > \text{Epi Inf} = \text{placebo} .$$

In both the euphoria and the anger conditions, emotional level in the Epi Inf condition is considerably less than that achieved in any of the other Epi conditions. The results for the placebo condition, however, are ambiguous, since the placebo subjects consistently fall between the Epi Ign and the Epi Inf subjects. This is a particularly troubling pattern because it makes it impossible to evaluate unequivocally the effects of the state of physiological arousal, and indeed raises serious questions about the entire theoretical structure. Though the emotional level is consistently greater in the Epi Mis and Epi Ign conditions than in the placebo condition, this difference is significant at acceptable probability levels only on the behavioral indices in the anger conditions.

In order to explore the problem further, let us examine experimental factors that might have acted to restrain the emotional level in the Epi Ign and Epi Mis conditions. Clearly the ideal test of the first two hypotheses requires an experimental setup in which the subject has flatly no way of evaluating his state of physiological arousal other than by means of the experimentally provided cognitions. Had it been possible to produce physiologically a state of sympathetic activation by means other than injection, one could have approached this experimental ideal more closely than in the present setup. As it stands, however, there is always a reasonable alternative cognition available to the aroused subject—he feels the way he does because of the injection. To the extent that the subject seizes on such an explanation of his bodily state, we should expect that he will be uninfluenced by the stooge.

It is possible, fortunately, to examine the effect of this artifact. In answers to open-end questions in which subjects described their own mood and physical state, some of the Epi Ign and Epi Mis subjects clearly attributed their physical state to the injection, saying, e.g., "the shot gave me the shivers." In effect, these subjects are self-informed. Comparing these subjects with the remaining subjects in a condition, one finds in the anger Epi Ign condition that self-informed subjects are considerably less angry than the remaining subjects. Similarly in the euphoria Epi Mis and Epi Ign conditions, self-informed subjects are considerably less euphoric than their non-self-informed counterparts. If one eliminates such self-informed subjects, the differences between the placebo and Epi Ign or Epi Mis conditions become highly significant statistically in both the anger and the euphoria set of conditions. Clearly, indications are good that this self-informing artifact has attenuated the effects of epinephrine.

Let us examine next the fact that, consistently, the emotional level in placebo conditions is higher than that in the Epi Inf conditions.

Theoretically, of course, it should be expected that the level in the two conditions will be equally low, for by assuming that emotional state is a joint function of a state of physiological arousal and the appropriateness of a cognition, we are, in effect, assuming a multiplicative function, so that if either component is at zero, emotional level is at zero. This expectation should hold, however, only if we can be sure that there is no sympathetic activation in the placebo conditions. This assumption, of course, is completely unrealistic, since the injection of placebo does not prevent sympathetic activation. The experimental situations were fairly dramatic, and certainly some of the placebo subjects must have experienced physiological arousal. If this general line of reasoning is correct, it should be anticipated that the emotional level of subjects who give indications of sympathetic activity will be greater than that of subjects who do not.

Since in all conditions a subject's pulse was taken before the injection and again after the session with the stooge, there is one index of sympathetic activation available—change in pulse rate. The predominant pattern in the placebo conditions was, of course, a decrease in pulse rate. It will be assumed, therefore, that in the placebo conditions, those subjects whose pulses increase or remain the same give indications of sympathetic arousal, whereas those subjects whose pulses decrease do not. Comparing, within placebo conditions, such self-aroused subjects with those who give no indication of sympathetic activation, we find in the anger condition that those subjects whose pulses increase or remain the same are considerably and significantly angrier than those subjects whose pulses decrease. Similarly, in the euphoria placebo condition, the self-aroused subjects are considerably and significantly more euphoric than the subjects who give no indication of sympathetic activation. As expected, sympathetic activation accompanies an increase in emotional level.

It should be noted, too, on the several indices, that the emotional levels of subjects who show no signs of sympathetic activity are quite close to the emotional levels of subjects in the parallel Epi Inf conditions. The similarity of these sets of scores and their uniformly low level of indicated emotionality would certainly make it appear that both factors are essential to an emotional state. When either the level of sympathetic arousal is low or a completely appropriate cognition is available, the level of emotionality is low.

Let us summarize the major findings of this experiment and examine the extent to which they support the propositions offered at the beginning of this chapter. It has been suggested, first, that given a state of physiological arousal for which an individual has no explanation, he will label this state in terms of the cognitions available to him. This implies, of course, that by manipulating the cognitions of an individual in such a state, we can manipulate his feelings in diverse directions. Experimental results support this proposition, since after the injection of epinephrine, those subjects who had no explanation for the bodily state thus produced, proved readily manipulable into the disparate feeling states of euphoria and anger.

From this first proposition, it must follow that given a state of physiological arousal for which the individual has a completely satisfactory explanation, he will not label this state in terms of the alternative cognitions available. Experimental evidence strongly supports this expectation. In those conditions in which subjects were injected with epinephrine and told precisely what they would feel and why, they proved relatively immune to any effects of the manipulated cognitions. In the anger condition, these subjects did not become at all angry; in the euphoria condition, these subjects reported themselves to be far less happy than subjects with an identical bodily state but no adequate knowledge of why they felt the way they did.

Finally, it has been suggested that given constant cognitive circumstances, an individual will react emotionally only to the extent that he experiences a state of physiological arousal. Without taking account of experimental artifacts, the evidence in support of this proposition is consistent but tentative. When the effects of "self-informing" tendencies in epinephrine subjects and of "self-arousing" tendencies in placebo subjects are partialed out, the evidence strongly supports the proposition.

The pattern of data, then, falls neatly into line with theoretical expectations. However, the fact that we were forced to rely to some extent on internal analyses in order to partial out the effects of experimental artifacts inevitably makes these conclusions somewhat tentative. In order further to test these propositions on the interaction of cognitive and physiological determinants of emotional state, a series of additional experiments was designed to rule out or overcome the operation of these artifacts.

The first of these experiments was designed by Schachter and

Wheeler (1962) to test, by extending the range of manipulated sympathetic activation, the proposition that emotionality is positively related to physiological arousal. It seemed clear from the results of the study just described that the self-arousing tendency of placebo subjects tended to obscure the differences between placebo and epinephrine conditions. A test of the proposition at stake, then, would require a comparison of subjects who have received injections of epinephrine with subjects who are rendered incapable, to some extent, of self-activation of the sympathetic nervous system. Thanks to a class of drugs known generally as autonomic blocking agents, such blocking is, to some degree, possible. If it is correct that a state of sympathetic discharge is a necessary component of an emotional experience, it should be anticipated that whatever emotional state is experimentally manipulated should be experienced most strongly by subjects who have received epinephrine, next by placebo subjects, and least of all by subjects who have received injections of an autonomic blocking agent.

In order to conceal the purposes of the study and the nature of the injection, the experiment was again cast in the framework of a study of the effects of vitamins on vision. As soon as a subject (again, subjects were male college students) arrived, he was taken to a private room and told by the experimenter:

I've asked you to come today to take part in an experiment concerning the effects of vitamins on the visual processes. Our experiment is concerned with the effects of Suproxin on vision. Suproxin is a high-concentrate vitamin C derivative. If you agree to take part in the experiment, we will give you an injection of Suproxin and then subject your retina to about fifteen minutes of continuous black and white stimulation. This is simpler than it sounds: we'll just have you watch a black and white movie. After the movie, we'll give you a series of visual tests.

The injection itself is harmless and will be administered by our staff doctor. It may sting a little at first, as most injections do, but after this you will feel nothing and will have no side effects. We know that some people dislike getting injections, and if you take part in the experiment, we want it to be your own decision. Would you like to?

All subjects agreed to take part. There were three forms of Suproxin administered—epinephrine, placebo, and chlorpromazine.

1. Epinephrine: Subjects in this condition received a subcutaneous injection of ½ cc of a 1:1000 solution of Winthrop Laboratories' Suprarenin.

2. Placebo: Subjects in this condition received a subcutaneous injection of ½ cc of saline solution.

3. Chlorpromazine: Subjects in this condition received an intramuscular injection of a solution consisting of 1 cc (25 mg) of Smith, Kline & French Thorazine and 1 cc of saline solution.

The choice of chlorpromazine as a blocking agent was dictated by considerations of safety, ease of administration, and known duration of effect. Ideally, one would have wished for a blocking agent whose mechanism and effect were precisely and solely the reverse of those of epinephrine—a peripherally acting agent that would prevent the excitation of sympathetically innervated structures. Though it is certainly possible to approach this ideal more closely with agents other than chlorpromazine, such drugs tend to be dangerous, or difficult to administer, or of short duration.

Chlorpromazine is known to act as a sympathetic depressant. It has a moderate hypotensive effect, with a slight compensatory increase in heart rate. It has mild adrenergic blocking activity, since it reverses the pressor effects of small doses of epinephrine and depresses responses of the nictitating membrane to preganglionic stimulation. Killam (1959) summarizes what is known and supposed about the mechanism of action of chlorpromazine as follows: "Autonomic effects in general may be attributed to a mild peripheral adrenergic blocking activity and probably to central depression of sympathetic centers, possibly in the hypothalamus." Popularly, of course, the compound is known as a "tranquilizer."

It is known that chlorpromazine has effects other than the sympatholytic effect of interest to us. For purposes of experimental purity this is unfortunate but inevitable in this sort of research. It is clear, however, that the three conditions do differ in the degree of manipulated sympathetic activation.

Rather than the more complicated devices employed in the previous experiment, an emotion-inducing film was used as a means of manipulating the cognitive component of emotional states. In deciding on the type of film, two extremes seemed possible—a horror-, fright-, or anxiety-provoking film, or a comic, amusement-provoking film. Since it is a common stereotype that adrenalin makes one nervous and that the tranquilizer, chlorpromazine, makes one tranquil and mildly euphoric, the predicted pattern of results with a horror film would be subject to alternative interpretation. It was deliberately decided, then, to use a comedy. If my hypothesis is correct, it should be anticipated that epinephrine subjects would find the film somewhat funnier than placebo subjects who, in turn, would be more amused than chlorpromazine subjects.

The film chosen was a 14-minute excerpt from a Jack Carson movie called "The Good Humor Man." This excerpt is a self-contained, comprehensible episode involving a slapstick chase scene.

Three subjects, one from each of the drug conditions, always watched the film simultaneously. The projection room was deliberately arranged so that the subjects could neither see nor hear one another. Facing the screen were three theater-type seats separated from one another by large, heavy partitions. In a further attempt to maintain the independence of the subjects, the sound volume of the projector was turned up to mask any sounds made by the subjects.

The subjects' reactions while watching the film were used as the chief index of amusement. During the showing of the movie an observer, who had been introduced as an assistant who would help administer the visual tests, systematically scanned the subjects and recorded their reactions to the film. He observed each subject once every 10 seconds, so that over the course of the film 88 units of each subject's behavior were categorized. The observer simply recorded each subject's reaction to the film according to the following scheme:

a. Neutral: straight-faced watching of film with no indication of amusement.

b. Smile.

c. Grin: a smile with teeth showing.

d. Laugh: a smile or grin on face accompanied by bodily movements usually associated with laughter, e.g., shaking shoulders, moving head.

e. Big laugh: belly laugh; a laugh accompanied by violent body movement such as doubling up, throwing up hands.

In a minute-by-minute comparison, two independent observers agreed in their categorization of 90 per cent of the 528 units recorded in six different reliability trials.

The observer, of course, never knew which subject had received which injection.

The observation record provides a continuous record of each subject's reaction to the film. As an over-all index of amusement, the number of units in which a subject's behavior was recorded in the categories "smile," "grin," "laugh," and "big laugh" are summed together. The means of this amusement index are presented in Table 3. The larger the figure, the more amusement was manifest. Differences are in the anticipated direction. Epinephrine subjects gave indications of greater amusement than placebo subjects who, in turn, were more amused than chlorpromazine subjects.

TABLE 3

The Effects of Epinephrine, Placebo, and Chlorpromazine on Amusement

Condition	N	Mean amusement index
Epinephrine	38	17.79
Placebo	42	14.31
Chlorpromazine	46	10.41

Values of p: Epi vs. placebo, n.s.; Epi vs. chlorpromazine, $<.01$; placebo vs. chlorpromazine, $<.05$.

Though the trend is clearly in the predicted direction, epinephrine and placebo subjects do not differ significantly in this over-all index. The difference between these two groups, however, becomes apparent when we examine strong ("laugh" and "big laugh") reactions to the film; we find an average of 4.84 such units among the epinephrine subjects and of only 1.83 such units among placebo subjects. This difference is significant at better than the .05 level of significance. Epinephrine subjects tend to be openly amused at the film, placebo subjects to be quietly amused. Some 16 per cent of epinephrine subjects reacted at some point with belly laughs, whereas not a single placebo subject did so. It should be noted that this is much the state of affairs one would expect from the disguised injection of epinephrine—a manipulation which, as has been suggested, creates a bodily state "in search of" an appropriate cognition. Certainly laughter can be considered a more appropriate accompaniment to the state of sympathetic arousal than can quietly smiling.

It would appear, then, that the degree of overt amusement is directly related to the degree of manipulated sympathetic activation.

A further test of the relationship of emotionality to sympathetic activity was made by Singer (1963), who in a deliberate attempt to rule out the operation of the self-informing artifact, conducted his study on rats—a species unlikely to attribute an aroused physiological state to an injection. Among other things, Singer examined the effects of injections of epinephrine (an intraperitoneal injection of epinephrine suspended in peanut oil in a concentration of 0.10 mg per kilogram of body weight) and placebo on the reactions of rats to standard frightening situations. His technique was simple. In fright conditions, he placed his animals in a box containing a doorbell, a door buzzer, and a flashing 150-watt bulb. After a brief interval a switch was tripped, setting off all three devices simultaneously for a 1½-minute interval. In non-fright conditions, of course, the switch was never tripped.

Singer's results are presented in Table 4. The figures presented in this table represent an index whose components are generally accepted indicators of fright, such as defecation, urination, and the like. The larger the figure the more frightened the animal. Clearly there is a substantial drug-related difference in the fright condition, and no difference at all in the non-fright condition. The drug–stress interaction is significant at better than the .01 level of confidence. It would certainly appear that under these experimental circumstances the state of fear is related to sympathetic activity. Further evidence for this relationship is found in a study conducted by Latané and Schachter (1962), which demonstrated that rats injected with epinephrine were notably more capable of avoidance learning than rats injected with a placebo. Using a modified Miller-Mowrer shuttlebox, these investigators found that during an experimental period involving 200 massed trials, fifteen rats injected with epinephrine avoided shock an average of 101.2 trials, whereas fifteen placebo-injected rats averaged only 37.3 avoidances.

TABLE 4

The Relationship of Epinephrine to Fright

Condition	Epinephrine	Placebo	p value of difference
Fright	13.15	11.49	.025
Non-fright	7.47	7.17	n.s.

In each of the four conditions, $N = 12$.

Discussion and Implications

Taken together, this body of studies does give strong support to the propositions that generated these experimental tests. Given a state of sympathetic activation for which no immediately appropriate explanation is available, human subjects can be readily manipulated into states of euphoria, of anger, and of amusement at a movie. Varying the intensity of sympathetic activation serves to vary the intensity of a number of different emotional states in both rat and human subjects. Clearly the line of thought guiding these experiments is modified Jamesianism, since emotion is viewed as visceral activity in interaction with cognitive or situational factors. Let us examine the extent to which the addition of cognitive elements allows us to cope with the shortcomings of a purely visceral formulation. Since Cannon's critique (1927, 1929) has been the most lucid and influential attack on a visceral view of emotion, I shall focus discussion around Cannon's five criticisms of the James-Lange theory.

A Re-examination of Cannon's Critique of a Visceral Formulation of Emotion

Criticisms Overcome by Cognitive Considerations

1. Cannon's criticism that "artificial induction of the visceral changes typical of strong emotions does not produce them" is based on the results of Marañon's (1924) study and its several replications. The fact that the injection of adrenalin produces apparently genuine emotional states in only a tiny minority of subjects is, of course, completely damning for a theory that equates visceral activity with affect. This is, on the other hand, precisely the fact that inspired the series of studies described earlier. Rather than being a criticism, the fact that the injection of adrenalin, in and of itself, does not lead to an emotional state is one of the strong points of the present formulation, since, with the addition of cognitive propositions, we are able to specify and manipulate the conditions under which such an injection will or will not lead to an emotional state.

2. Cannon's point that "the same visceral changes occur in very different emotional states" is again damning for a purely visceral viewpoint. Since we are aware of a great variety of feeling and emotion states, it must follow from a purely visceral formulation that the variety of emotions will be accompanied by an equal variety of dif-

ferentiable bodily states. Though the evidence as of today is by no means as one-sided as it appeared in Cannon's day, it does seem that the gist of Cannon's criticism is still correct. Following James's pronouncement, a formidable number of studies were undertaken in search of the physiological differentiators of the emotions. The results, in those early days, were almost always failure to find any. All of the emotional states experimentally manipulated were characterized by a general pattern of activation of the sympathetic nervous system, but there appeared to be no clear-cut physiological discriminators of the various emotions.

More recent work, however, has given some indication that there may be differentiators. Ax (1953) and Schachter (1957) studied fear and anger. On a large number of indices both of these states were characterized by a similar high level of sympathetic activation, but on several indices they did differ in the degree of activation. Wolf and Wolff (1947) studied a subject with a gastric fistula and were able to distinguish two patterns in the physiological responses of the stomach wall. It should be noted, though, that for many months they studied their subject during and following a great variety of moods and emotions, but were able to distinguish only two patterns.

Whether there are physiological distinctions among the various emotional states must still be considered an open question. Recent work might be taken to indicate that such differences are at best rather subtle, and that the variety of emotion, mood, and feeling states is by no means matched by an equal variety of visceral patterns—a state of affairs hardly compatible with the Jamesian formulation. On the other hand, the question of the physiological differentiability of the various emotions is essentially irrelevant to the present formulation, which maintains simply that cognitive and situational factors determine the labels applied to any of a variety of states of physiological arousal.

The experimental search for the physiological differentiators of emotional states has involved such substantial, long-time effort that I would like to comment further on the problem. Taken together, these experiments have yielded inconclusive results. Most, though not all, of these studies have indicated no differences among the various emotional states. Since as human beings, rather than as scientists, we have no difficulty identifying, labeling, and distinguishing among our feelings, the results of these studies have long seemed rather puzzling and paradoxical. Perhaps because of this, there has been a persistent tendency to discount such results as being due to ignorance or to methodological inadequacy and to pay far more attention to the very few studies that demonstrate *some* sort of physiological differences among emotional states than to the very many studies that indicate no differences at all. It is conceivable, however, that these results should be taken at face value and that emotional states may, indeed, be generally characterized by a high level of sympathetic activation with few, if any, physiological distinguishers among the many emotional states. If this is so, the cognitive-physiological formulation I have outlined and the findings of the studies I have described may help to resolve the problem. Obviously these studies do *not* rule out the possibility of differences among the emotional states. However, given precisely the same state of epinephrine-induced sympathetic activation, we have, by means of cognitive manipulations, been able to produce in our subjects the very disparate states of euphoria, anger, and amusement at a movie. It may, indeed, be the case that cognitive factors are major determiners of the emotional "labels" we apply to a common state of sympathetic arousal.

A novelist's statement of this position is Ambler's (1958) description of a fugitive who introspects:

"Rather to his surprise, he found that being wanted for murder produced in him an effect almost identical to that of a dentist's waiting-room—a sense of discomfort in the intestinal region, a certain constriction in the chest. He supposed that the same glands discharged the same secretions into the blood stream in both cases. Nature could be absurdly parsimonious."

If these speculations are correct, nature may indeed be far more parsimonious than Ambler suggests.

3. Cannon's point that "the viscera are relatively insensitive structures" is again telling for a formulation which virtually requires a richness of visceral sensation in order to be able to match the presumed richness of emotional experience. For the present formulation, of course, the criticism is irrelevant. Just so long as there is *some* visceral or cardiovascular sensation, the cognitive-physiological hypotheses are applicable.

The introduction of cognitive factors does allow us, then, to cope with three of Cannon's criticisms of a purely visceral formulation. Let us turn next to Cannon's remaining two points, which are quite as troublesome for the present view of emotion as for the Jamesian view.

Visceral Separation and Emotion

Cannon's remaining criticisms are these: "visceral changes are too slow to be a source of emotional feeling" (i.e., the latency period of arousal of many visceral structures is longer than the latency of onset of emotional feelings reported in introspective studies), and "total separation of the viscera from the central nervous system does not alter emotional behavior." Both criticisms make essentially the same point, since they identify conditions in which there are apparently emotions unaccompanied by visceral activity. The data with which Cannon buttresses his latter criticism are based on his own studies (Cannon, Lewis, and Britton, 1927) of sympathectomized cats, and Sherrington's (1900) study of sympathectomized dogs. For both sets of experimental animals "the absence of reverberation from the viscera did not alter in any respect the appropriate emotional display; its only abbreviation was surgical." In the presence of a barking dog, for example, the sympathectomized cats manifested almost all of the signs of feline rage. Finally, Cannon notes the report of Dana (1921) that a patient with a spinal-cord lesion and almost totally without visceral sensation still manifested normal emotionality.*

For either the Jamesian or the present formulation such data are crucial, since both views demand visceral arousal as a necessary condition for emotional arousal. When faced with this evidence, James's defenders (e.g., Wenger, 1950; Mandler, 1962) have consistently made the point that the apparently emotional behavior manifested by sympathectomized animals and men is well-learned behavior, acquired long before sympathectomy. There is a dual implication in this position: first, that sympathetic arousal facilitates the acquisition of emotional behavior, and, second, that sympathectomized subjects

---

* More recent work supporting Cannon's position is that of Moyer and Bunnell (Moyer, 1958a, 1958b; Moyer and Bunnell, 1959, 1960a, 1960b), who in an extensive series of studies of bilaterally adrenalectomized rats have consistently failed to find any indication of differences between experimental and control animals on a variety of emotionally linked behaviors such as avoidance learning. The effects of adrenalectomy are by no means clear-cut, however, for other investigators (Levine and Soliday, 1962) have found distinct differences between operated and control animals.

act but do not feel emotional. There is a small but growing body of evidence supporting these contentions. Wynne and Solomon (1955) have demonstrated that sympathectomized dogs acquire an avoidance response considerably more slowly than control dogs. Further, on extinction trials most of their 13 sympathectomized animals extinguished quickly, whereas not a single one of 30 control dogs gave any indications of extinction over 200 trials. Of particular interest are two dogs who were sympathectomized after they had acquired the avoidance response. On extinction trials these two animals behaved precisely like the control dogs—giving no indication of extinction. Thus, when deprived of visceral innervation, animals are quite slow in acquiring emotionally-linked avoidance responses and, in general, quick to extinguish such responses. When deprived of visceral innervation only after acquisition, the animals behave exactly like the normal dogs—they fail to extinguish. A true Jamesian would undoubtedly note that these latter animals have learned to act as if they were emotional, but would ask: do they feel emotional?

This apparently unanswerable question seems on its way to being answered in a thoroughly fascinating study of the emotional life of paraplegics and quadriplegics conducted by Hohmann (1962). Hohmann studied a sample of 25 patients of the Spinal Cord Injury Service of the Veterans Administration Hospital at Long Beach, California. The subjects were divided into five groups according to the height of the clinically complete lesions as follows:

Group I, with lesions between the second and eighth cervical segmental level, have only the cranial branch of the parasympathetic nervous system remaining intact.

Group II, with lesions between the first and fourth thoracic segmental level, have, in addition to the above, at least partial innervation of the sympathetically innervated cardiac plexus remaining intact.

Group III, with lesions between the sixth and twelfth thoracic segmental level, have, additionally, at least partial innervation of the splanchnic outflow of the sympathetics remaining intact.

Group IV, with lesions between the first and fifth lumbar segmental level, have, in addition, at least partial sympathetic innervation of the mesenteric ganglia.

Group V, with lesions between the first and fifth sacral segments, have, in addition, at least partial innervation of the sacral branch of the parasympathetic nervous system.

These groups, then, fall along a continuum of visceral innervation and sensation. The higher the lesion, the less the visceral sensation. If the present conception of emotion is correct, one should expect to find decreasing manifestation of emotion as the height of the lesion increases.

With each of his subjects Hohmann conducted an extensive, structured interview, which was "directed to specific feelings in situations of sexual excitement, fear, anger, grief, and sentimentality, and the subjects' attention was directed toward their feelings rather than to the concomitant ideation." Hohmann asked his subjects to recall an emotion-arousing incident prior to their injury and a comparable incident following the injury. They were then asked to compare the intensity of their emotional experiences before and after injury. Changes in reported affect comprise the body of data. I have adapted Hohmann's data for presentation in Fig. 1. Following Hohmann's coding schema, a report of no change is scored as 0; a report of mild change (e.g., "I feel it less, I guess") is scored −1 for a decrease and +1 for an increase; a report of strong change (e.g., "I feel it a helluva lot less") is scored as −2 or +2.

Hohmann's data for the states of fear and anger are plotted in Fig. 1. It can be immediately seen that the higher the lesion and the less the visceral sensation, the greater the decrease in emotionality. Precisely the same relationship holds for the states of sexual excitement and grief. The sole exception to this consistent trend is "sentimentality," which, I suspect, should be considered a cognitive rather than a "feeling" state. It is clear that for these cases, deprivation of visceral sensation has resulted in a marked decrease in emotionality.

If, in an attempt to assess the absolute level of emotionality of these cases one examines their verbalized introspections, one notes again and again that subjects with cervical lesions describe themselves as acting emotional but not feeling emotional. A few typical quotes follow:

"It's sort of cold anger. Sometimes I act angry when I see some injustice. I yell and cuss and raise hell, because if you don't do it sometimes, I've learned people will take advantage of you, but it just doesn't have the heat to it that it used to. It's a mental kind of anger."

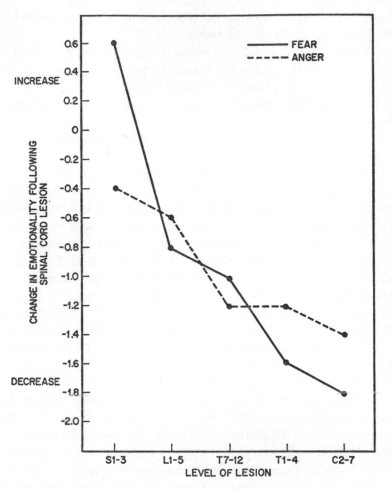

Fig. 1. Changes in emotionality as related to height of spinal cord lesion.
(Adapted from Hohmann, 1962.)

"Seems like I get thinking mad, not shaking mad, and that's a lot different."

"I say I am afraid, like when I'm going into a real stiff exam at school, but I don't really feel afraid, not all tense and shaky, with that hollow feeling in my stomach, like I used to."

In effect, these subjects seem to be saying that when the situation demands it, they make the proper emotional-appearing responses but they do not feel emotional. Parenthetically, it should be noted that these quotations bear an almost contrapuntal resemblance to the introspections of Marañon's subjects who, after receiving an injection of adrenalin, described their feelings in a way that led Marañon to label them "cold" or "as if" emotions. Many of these subjects described their physical symptoms and added statements such as "I feel as if I were very frightened; however, I am calm."

The two sets of introspections are like opposite sides of the same coin. Marañon's subjects report the visceral correlates of emotion, but in the absence of veridical cognitions do not describe themselves as feeling emotion. Hohmann's subjects describe the appropriate reaction to an emotion-inducing situation, but in the absence of visceral arousal do not seem to describe themselves as emotional. It is as if they were labeling a situation, not describing a feeling. Obviously, this contrasting set of introspections is precisely what should be anticipated from a formulation of emotion as a joint function of cognitive and physiological factors.

The line of thought stimulated by the Wynne and Solomon (1955) and the Hohmann (1962) studies may indeed be the answer to Cannon's observation that there can be emotional behavior without visceral activity. From the evidence of these studies, it would appear, first, that autonomic arousal greatly facilitates the acquisition of emotional behavior but is not necessary for its maintenance if the behavior is acquired prior to sympathectomy; and, second, that in the absence of autonomic arousal, behavior that appears emotional will not be experienced as emotional.

Some Effects of Cognitive Factors on the
Appraisal of Bodily States

Let us turn now to the cognitive component of this view of emotion and examine further implications of the formulation. The key cognitive assumption underlying the human experiments described is that "given a state of physiological arousal for which an individual has no immediate explanation, he will label this state and describe his feelings in terms of the cognitions available to him." Obviously, there is implicit in this proposition the motivational notion that a drive exists to evaluate, understand, and label ambiguous body states.

I am suggesting that Festinger's (1954) theoretical invention—the "evaluative need" he employs as the conceptual underpinning of his theory of social comparison processes—is as necessary and useful for an understanding of emotion and the perception of bodily states as it has proven for an understanding of the opinions. Given a new, strange, or ambiguous bodily state, the individual will feel pressures to decide exactly what it is that he feels and to decide how he will label these feelings. In the Schachter and Singer (1962) study, the differences between the Epi Ign and Epi Inf conditions would certainly indicate that it is useful to apply this notion of evaluative needs to bodily states.

These cognitive assumptions, as worded, clearly imply applicability to bodily states other than the epinephrine-induced state of sympathetic activation. If these ideas are correct, it should be expected that any novel bodily state will give rise to pressures to decide what is felt, to decide how these feelings are to be labeled, and, perhaps, to decide whether these feelings are pleasant or unpleasant ones. Though I know of no experiments directly designed to test these ideas for states other than that induced by epinephrine, the extensive literature on the effects of drugs provides many hints and bits of data which suggest that these ideas do have wide applicability.

As an example, let us consider the effects of smoking marihuana. According to pharmacological texts, marihuana or cannabis produces the following physiological effects:

Marihuana usually causes an increase in pulse rate, a slight rise in blood pressure, and conjunctival vascular congestion; the cardiovascular system is otherwise unaffected. The blood sugar and basal metabolic rate are elevated, but usually not beyond the upper limits of normal. Urinary frequency without diuresis occurs. A marked increase in appetite (especially for sweets) and hunger are characteristic, and hypergeusia may occasionally be prominent. Dryness of the mouth and throat is frequent. Nausea, vomiting, and occasionally diarrhea may be noted.

Tremor, ataxia, vertigo, tinnitus, hyper-reflexia, increased sensitivity to touch, pressure, and pain stimuli, pupillary dilatation with sluggish light reflexes, and a sensation of floating are also observed. . . . Tremulousness of the eyelids, lips, and tongue and nystagmus on lateral gaze are common. (Goodman and Gilman, 1958, pp. 172–73.)

These are the measured physiological changes caused by smoking marihuana. In and of themselves, are such bodily feelings pleasant or unpleasant? Given such symptoms, should the smoker describe himself as "high" or as "sick"?

In an absorbing study of fifty marihuana users, the sociologist Becker (1953) reports an invariable sequence in learning to use marihuana for pleasure. Once he has learned the techniques of smoking, the smoker must learn to label his physiological symptoms as being "high." In Becker's words,

Being high consists of two elements: the presence of symptoms caused by marihuana use and the recognition of these symptoms and their connection by the user with his use of the drug. It is not enough, that is, that the effects be present; they alone do not automatically provide the experience of being high. The user must be able to point them out to himself and consciously connect them with his having smoked marihuana before he can have this experience. Otherwise, regardless of the actual effects produced, he considers that the drug has had no effect on him.

An example of learning that he is high is provided by this quotation from a novice who gets high for the first time only after he learns that intense hunger is one consequence of smoking marihuana:

They were just laughing the hell out of me because like I was eating so much. I just scoffed [ate] so much food, and they were just laughing at me, you know. Sometimes I'd be looking at them, you know, wondering why they're laughing, you know, not knowing what I was doing. [Well, did they eventually tell you why they were laughing?] Yeah, yeah, I come back, "Hey, man, what's happening?" and all of a sudden I feel weird, you know. "Man, you're on you know. You're on pot [high on marihuana]." I said, "No, am I?" Like I don't know what's happening.

An instance of more indirect learning is the following: "I heard little remarks that were made by people. Somebody said, 'My legs are rubbery,' and I can't remember all the remarks that were made because I was very attentively listening for all these cues for what I was supposed to feel like."

Obviously, these are instances where the novice must literally learn to notice his feelings. Given that a user is made aware of his symptoms and has learned that what he is feeling is being "high," Becker notes that one further step is necessary for continued use of the drug:

He must learn to enjoy the effects he has just learned to experience. Marihuana-produced sensations are not automatically or necessarily pleasurable. The taste for such experience is a socially acquired one, not different in kind from acquired tastes for oysters or dry martinis. The user feels dizzy, thirsty;

his scalp tingles; he misjudges time and distances, and so on. Are these things pleasurable? He isn't sure. If he is to continue marihuana use, he must decide that they are. Otherwise, getting high, while a real enough experience, will be an unpleasant one he would rather avoid.

Becker supports this analysis with numerous instances of novice smokers' being taught, in social interaction, that their feelings were pleasant.

This study, then, indicates that new marihuana users must be taught to notice and identify what they feel, must be taught to label the state as "high" and must be taught that the state is "pleasant." The marihuana-induced state of feelings appears to be another instance of a bodily state that takes its meaning and labels in good part from cognitive and social factors.

I would guess that the labels and hedonic valuation attached to an amazing variety of bodily conditions are cognitively determined. Obviously, there are limits. It is unlikely that anyone with undiagnosed peritonitis could ever be convinced that he was euphoric, high, or anything but deathly ill. I suspect, though, that the limits are astonishingly wide. Vomiting to us may seem unpleasant, but to a banqueting Roman gourmet it may have been one of the exquisite pleasures.

One final point. If it is correct that the labels attached to feeling states are cognitively, situationally, or socially determined, it is clearly possible that an uncommon or inappropriate label can be attached to a feeling state. Where such is the case, we may anticipate bizarre and pathological behavior. As an example of this possibility, consider the state of hunger. We are so accustomed to think of hunger as a primary motive, innate and wired into the animal, unmistakable in its cues, that even the possibility that an organism would be incapable of correctly labeling the state seems too farfetched to credit. The physiological changes accompanying food deprivation seem distinct, identifiable, and unvarying. Yet even a moment's consideration will make it clear that attaching the label "hunger" to this set of bodily feelings and behaving accordingly, is a learned, socially determined, cognitive act. Consider the neonate. Wholly at the mercy of its feelings, when uncomfortable, or in pain, or frightened, or hungry, or thirsty, it screams. Whether it is comforted, or soothed, or clucked at, or fondled, or fed has little to do with the state of its own feelings, but depends entirely on the ability and willingness of its mother or nurse to recognize the proper cues. If she is experienced, she will comfort the baby when he is frightened, soothe him when he is chafed, feed him when he is hungry, and so on. If she is inexperienced, her behavior may be completely inappropriate to the child's state. Most commonly, perhaps, the compassionate but bewildered mother will feed her child at any sign of distress.

It is precisely this state of affairs that the analyst Hilde Bruch (1961) suggests is at the heart of chronic obesity. Such cases she describes as characterized by a confusion between intense emotional states and hunger. During childhood these patients have not been taught to discriminate between hunger and such states as fear, anger, and anxiety. If this theory is correct, these people are, in effect, labeling a state of sympathetic activation as hunger. Small wonder that they are both fat and jolly.

References

Ambler, E. *Background to danger*. New York: Dell, 1958.

Ax, A. F. Physiological differentiation of emotional states. *Psychosom. Med.*, 1953, **15**, 433–42.

Becker, H. S. Becoming a marihuana user. *Amer. J. Sociol.*, 1953, **59**, 235–42.

Bruch, Hilde. Transformation of oral impulses in eating disorders: a conceptual approach. *Psychiat. Quart.*, 1961, **35**, 458–81.

Cannon, W. B. The James-Lange theory of emotions: a critical examination and an alternative theory. *Amer. J. Psychol.*, 1927, **39**, 106–24.

Cannon, W. B. *Bodily changes in pain, hunger, fear and rage*. (2d ed.) New York: D. Appleton, 1929.

Cannon, W. B., Lewis, J. T., and Britton, S. W. The dispensability of the sympathetic division of the autonomic system. *Boston Med. and Surg. J.*, 1927, **197**, 514.

Cantril, H., and Hunt, W. A. Emotional effects produced by the injection of adrenalin. *Amer. J. Psychol.*, 1932, **44**, 300–307.

Dana, C. L. The autonomic seat of the emotions: a discussion of the James-Lange theory. *A.M.A. Arch. Neurol. Psychiat.*, 1921, **6**, 634–39.

Festinger, L. A theory of social comparison processes. *Hum. Rel.*, 1954, **7**, 114–40.

Goodman, L. S., and Gilman, A. *The pharmacological basis of therapeutics*. New York: MacMillan, 1958.

Hohmann, G. W. The effect of dysfunctions of the autonomic nervous system on experienced feelings and emotions. Paper read at Conference on Emotions and Feelings at New School for Social Research, New York, Oct. 1962.

Hunt, J. McV., Cole, M. W., and Reis, E. C. Situational cues distinguishing anger, fear, and sorrow. *Amer. J. Psychol.*, 1958, 71, 136–51.

James, W. *The principles of psychology.* New York: Henry Holt, 1890. P. 449.

Killam, Eva K. The pharmacological aspects of certain drugs useful in psychiatry. In J. O. Cole and R. W. Gerard (Eds.), *Psychopharmacology: problems in evaluation.* National Academy of Sciences, National Research Council Publication 583, 1959. Pp. 20–45.

Landis, C., and Hunt, W. A. Adrenalin and emotion. *Psychol. Rev.*, 1932, 39, 467–85.

Latané, B., and Schachter, S. Adrenalin and avoidance learning. *J. comp. physiol. Psychol.*, 1962, 65, 369–72.

Levine, S., and Soliday, S. An effect of adrenal demedullation on the acquisition of a conditioned avoidance response. *J. comp. physiol. Psychol.*, 1962, 55, 214–16.

Mandler, G. Emotion. In R. Brown, *et al.*, *New directions in psychology.* New York: Holt, Rinehart and Winston, 1962. Pp. 267–343.

Marañon, G. Contribution à l'étude de l'action émotive de l'adrénaline. *Rev. française d'Endocrinologie*, 1924, 2, 301–25.

Moyer, K. E. Effect of adrenalectomy on anxiety-motivated behavior. *J. genet. Psychol.*, 1958a, 92, 11–16.

Moyer, K. E. Effect of adrenalectomy on emotional elimination. *J. genet. Psychol.*, 1958b, 92, 17–21.

Moyer, K. E., and Bunnell, B. N. Effect of adrenal demedullation on an avoidance response in the rat. *J. comp. physiol. Psychol.*, 1959, 52, 215–16.

Moyer, K. E., and Bunnell, B. N. Effects of adrenal demedullation on the startle response of the rat. *J. genet. Psychol.*, 1960a, 97, 341–44.

Moyer, K. E., and Bunnell, B. N. Effect of adrenal demedullation, operative stress and noise stress on emotional elimination. *J. genet. Psychol.*, 1960b, 96, 375–82.

Ruckmick, C. A. *The psychology of feeling and emotion.* New York: McGraw-Hill, 1936.

Schachter, J. Pain, fear, and anger in hypertensives and normotensives: a psychophysiologic study. *Psychosom. Med.*, 1957, 19, 17–29.

Schachter, S. *The psychology of affiliation.* Stanford, Calif.: Stanford Univ. Press, 1959.

Schachter, S., and Wheeler, L. Epinephrine, chlorpromazine, and amusement. *J. abnorm. soc. Psychol.*, 1962, 65, 121–28.

Schachter, S., and Singer, J. Cognitive, social and physiological determinants of emotional state. *Psychol. Rev.*, 1962, 69, 379–99.

Sherrington, C. S. Experiments on the value of vascular and visceral factors for the genesis of emotion. *Proc. Roy. Soc.*, 1900, 66, 390–403.

Singer, J. E. Sympathetic activation, drugs and fright. *J. comp. physiol. Psychol.*, 1963, 56, 612–15.

Wenger, M. A. Emotion as visceral action: an extension of Lange's theory. In Reymert, M. L., *Feelings and emotions:* the Mooseheart Symposium. New York: McGraw-Hill, 1950. Pp. 3–10.

Wolf, S., and Wolff, H. G. *Human gastric function.* New York: Oxford Univ. Press, 1947.

Woodworth, R. S., and Schlosberg, H. *Experimental psychology.* New York: Holt, 1954.

Wrightsman, L. S. Effects of waiting with others on changes in level of felt anxiety. *J. abnorm. soc. Psychol.,* 1960, **61**, 216–22.

Wynne, L. C., and Solomon, R. L. Traumatic avoidance learning: acquisition and extinction in dogs deprived of normal peripheral autonomic function. *Genet. psychol. Monogr.,* 1955, **52**, 241–84.

Experimental Exploration of the Et-epimeletic or Care-Soliciting Behavioral System

J. P. SCOTT AND F. H. BRONSON, *The Jackson Laboratory*

In Benjamin Franklin's day, when he and other enlightened citizens first began to appreciate the potential powers of the scientific method, the most important human problems were those connected with the improvement of commerce and industry and the harnessing of physical energy. Today, we have not only harnessed forms of physical energy undreamed of two hundred years ago, and applied them successfully to commerce and industry; we have also made great strides in the control of biological disease. As these once-important problems move into the background, other human difficulties become more prominent. Among them we can list four major problems: warfare, overpopulation, poverty, and, last, but not least, the lack of happiness. All of these problems are basically connected with the understanding and control of social behavior, and this chapter reports the results of the psychobiological exploration of a hitherto neglected system of social behavior which develops early in life and is closely related to several major adult forms of social activity.

The Analysis of a Behavioral System

The Development of Behavior. In our analyses of social behavior we and our colleagues have long used a developmental approach (Scott, 1962). The detailed descriptive study of behavioral development soon made us aware that an animal lives in different sorts of environments at different periods of development, and has different capacities

The research reported in this chapter was supported by grant number MH-04481 from the National Institute of Mental Health.

at different ages which enable it to deal with the changing problems of adaptation that confront it. Sharp contrasts in both behavior and environmental conditions may be found in comparing one period with another.

The first period of mammalian life in which true behavior is seen is the fetal period. During this time all nutrition and elimination are accomplished through the placenta. The fetus has no need to breathe, and its surroundings are kept at a uniform temperature by the body of the mother. There is very little opportunity for tactile stimulation, and perhaps the most important stimuli that can penetrate from the outside are changes in pressure. The behavior of the fetus consists mostly of a series of reflexes that involve straightening the body and limbs, probably having the function of preventing adhesions and promoting circulation. Otherwise, the fetus lives in what appears to be a sleeping state.

At birth the infant mammal is presented with a whole new set of adaptational problems. Lowered oxygen tension causes it to breathe, and for the first time it comes in contact with lower temperature. Depending on the development of its sense organs, stimuli from light, sound, and odors may begin to elicit responses. However, the most vital behavioral problem of the neonatal infant is that of establishing a new method of nutrition. Food is obtainable through suckling, which for a mammal is the first form of ingestive behavior. In an animal like the dog, almost all behavior during the neonatal period centers around this behavior.

The growing puppy next passes through a brief period of some 5 to 7 days characterized by rapid transitions toward adult capacities. Both vision and hearing appear for the first time, and the puppy begins to walk instead of crawl. Its capacity for learning is greatly enhanced, and various patterns of adult social behavior appear. Following this transition period, there is an interval of several weeks in which the puppy has the capacity to make rapid emotional attachments, both with its mother and litter mates, and with the human beings who take care of it. This is called the period of primary socialization.

One of the most general conclusions from this sort of study is that behavioral capacities overlap periods of development beyond those in which they are primarily useful. This circumstance provides a

safety factor that has been evolved as an adaptation to meet the haz-
ards produced by accidental variations in the length of prenatal and
postnatal development. For example, reflexes that are useful only in
fetal life tend to remain until some time after birth, taking care of
the possibility of an extended pregnancy. The capacity for sucking
appears some time before birth, permitting even the premature infant
to cope with the environment. Moreover, this capacity does not disappear when the animal is weaned, but persists at least in some degree
throughout life. This suggests the possibility that there may be other
examples of capacities which are chiefly functional in infantile existence but which persist into adult life. Of these, one of the most prominent is that of et-epimeletic, or care-soliciting, behavior.

Et-epimeletic Behavior. The most striking thing about the behavior
of a neonatal puppy is the amount of noise it makes. No matter what
happens, whether the young puppy is cold, hungry, or hurt, it responds by vocalizing in a series of whines and yelps. The sounds of
these cries are highly variable, but so far we have been unable to
associate the cause of distress with any peculiarities of tone. When
highly distressed, whatever the cause, the puppy simply makes more
noise and vocalizes at a higher rate. We have hypothesized that the
variable nature of the sounds has the function of preventing auditory
accommodation in the listener.

It is obvious that the et-epimeletic behavior of the infant puppy
is organized into a primitive behavioral system. Being unable to
adapt to various situations by its own efforts, the puppy responds
by vocalizing, thus attracting the attention of its mother or of its
human caretakers. The function of this behavior is, of course, very
similar to that of crying in the human infant.

The human baby also has another form of et-epimeletic behavior,
the smiling response, which is used in a positive way rather than as
an adaptation to distress. This behavior first appears at about 5 weeks
of age, has the sole function of social stimulation, and communicates
a friendly attitude (Gewirtz, 1961). The corresponding type of behavior in the puppy is, of course, tail wagging, which likewise persists
throughout life, has only a social function, and indicates a friendly
approach.

The Development of Distress Vocalization. Research possibilities
connected with distress vocalization were first noticed by Emil Fred-

ericson (Scott, Fredericson, and Fuller, 1951), who was forcibly impressed by them during an experiment in which he took puppies away from their mothers and litter mates at different ages and reared them in his home. One puppy whined and yelped for 24 hours without a letup. Fredericson also observed that the vocalization of the younger puppies was chiefly caused by physical discomfort, in contrast to that of the older ones, who were much affected by being left alone.

Later experiments confirmed these impressions. During the neonatal and transition periods the puppy remains quiet as long as it is warm, well-fed, and unhurt. Records taken as puppies were weighed during these periods show that the rate of vocalization is maximum at birth or shortly afterward, and rapidly declines as the animals become able to stand and avoid contact with the cold metal of the scale.

Beginning at about 3 weeks of age, at the start of the period of socialization, a new cause of distress vocalization appears. Prior to this time the puppy will remain silent if warm, well-fed, and comfortable. Now he begins to vocalize in response to isolation. If kept in his home pen, the isolated puppy vocalizes at a moderate level, but if placed alone in a strange room or cage he becomes much more excited and vocalizes at a high rate. Elliot and Scott (1961) found that vocalization under the latter circumstances reaches a peak at 6 to 7 weeks of age and begins to decline thereafter. Animals experiencing isolation in a strange place for the first time show only slightly higher rates of vocalization than those of the same age who have had previous experience, indicating that the response is affected only slightly by habituation when the experience is repeated no oftener than once per week. Again, it is interesting that the response persists considerably beyond weaning and is found to some extent even in adult dogs.

Effect of Unfamiliarity or Strangeness. Fredericson (1950, 1952) did his first experiments by confining the puppies in small boxes, which suggested that confinement was part of the stimulus situation which evoked vocalization. Ross *et al.* (1960) placed puppies in small boxes on the floors of their home pens and obtained a higher rate of vocalization than if they were free. However, we found that if puppies are confined either in a small triangular squeeze box of the type used by Ross, or in a larger pen 2 feet square, there is no significant difference in the rate of vocalization (see Table 1). If anything, puppies yelp less in the smaller cage. Likewise, puppies vocalize at about the same rate if confined either in a small cage or in a strange room approximately the size of their home pens. It may be concluded that different degrees of confinement have no effect (at least until the puppy is painfully squeezed), and that confinement is meaningful only because it prevents the puppy from returning to its litter mates and home pen.

TABLE 1

Vocalizations per 10-Minute Period Under Two Different Degrees of Restraint

16 cocker spaniels 6 to 7 weeks old tested 4 times under each condition

Cage size	Mean	S.E.
Triangular floor, .56 sq. ft	1428	±62
Square floor, 4 sq. ft	1501	±48

We eventually used a two-foot cubical cage with wire bottom and opaque walls as a standard stimulus situation. The cage may be located within the home pen or in a strange room without altering the rate of response in puppies six to eight weeks old. However, puppies over 12 weeks of age rapidly become habituated if the cage is left in the same room. It may be concluded that unfamiliarity or strangeness is the important characteristic of the stimulus situation. Being alone in a strange place is potentially a highly dangerous situation for a young mammal, and distress vocalization is a built-in adaptive response in many species. The lost puppy vocalizes and so has a chance of attracting the attention of its parents or caretakers.

Effect of Duration of Experience. Fredericson (1950) showed that puppies given 1-minute periods of isolation interspersed with 1-minute periods of free handling and free movement vocalized at a rate only one-third as great as puppies given continuous 10-minute trials. He concluded that massed trials had a greater effect than distributed ones. Since then, we have done an experiment on 32 cocker spaniels between 6 and 8 weeks of age, measuring the yelping rates minute-by-minute for two consecutive 10-minute periods. Records show that the puppy usually does not begin to yelp at the full rate during the first minute. There is a tendency for the rate to increase during the second 10-minute period, particularly during the animal's first exposure to the situation. During four successive 20-minute trials on different days, the number of animals showing an increase during the second 10 minutes was 27, 24, 22, and 20.

In another experiment (Scott, Deshaies, and Morris, 1963), puppies were isolated in a strange cage overnight. Yelping rates were taken immediately after the pups were placed in isolation at 4 P.M. and at 8 A.M. the following morning, approximately 16 hours later. The rate went up by about 75 per cent in both basenji and Shetland sheepdog puppies. We can conclude that prolonged isolation in a strange place produces an important increase in the yelping rate, and that the puppies become more and more disturbed with the passage of time.

Experiments on Alleviation. Fredericson (1952) showed that placing two puppies together in a strange cage greatly reduced the amount of vocalization. This experiment was recently repeated in connection with an investigation of the effects of prior social stimulation on vocalization while in isolation. At 7 to 8 weeks of age, nine beagle pups were confined in a strange cage, either isolated or with a companion, for 10 minutes, and then immediately transferred to a second strange cage and confined for another 10 minutes. Each of the nine dogs was evaluated in each possible situation. The only reliable difference evident in the data (see Table 2) was a 75 per cent reduction of the yelping rate of pups confined with a companion.

Causey (1956) experimented with the effects of the presence of the mother, litter mates, and a fresh bone on the yelping of puppies removed to a strange room at different ages. There was much individual variation, but in general a litter mate was more effective than

TABLE 2

Alleviating Effect of a Companion Puppy

Mean Vocalization Rate for 10 Minutes in Nine Beagle Pups
7 to 8 Weeks of Age, in Consecutive Periods

| Cage | Order tested | |
	Paired-singly	Singly-singly
1	162*	825
2	800	903

* In presence of a second puppy; others tested alone.

the mother in reducing vocalization. A bone had approximately the same effect as either one, and after 10 weeks of age, when the vocalization rate had begun to decline sharply, the bone was more effective than either. Presumably this last effect is caused in part by the fact that the puppy cannot vocalize and chew at the same time. However, this pilot experiment suggests some interesting possibilities for studies on the relationship between eating or sucking and social isolation.

Experiments on the Interaction of Emotional States. Since, as far as it is known, all unpleasant emotions experienced by the puppy may be expressed as distress vocalization, it is possible to analyze the relationships between emotions by combining emotion-producing situations and observing their common effect upon this single variable. Such experiments have considerable relevance to basic problems concerned with abnormal behavior, since one of the elements in a situation leading to functionally induced maladaptive behavior is hypermotivation, which in itself may interfere with adaptation.

Theoretically, two kinds of emotions might be either mutually facilitating or mutually suppressing, or one might suppress the other. In accordance with the first supposition, all experiments confirm the conclusion that isolation and strangeness produce additive or facilitating effects (see Table 3). An animal that is isolated in its home pen yelps at a given rate, which is greatly increased in a strange pen or cage. The maximum effect of a strange situation is produced at 6 to 7 weeks of age, with the rate approximately three times that in the home pen.

TABLE 3

Effects of Combining Isolation and Strangeness

| | | | | Mean vocalizations per 10-minute period | |
| | | | | Home pen | Strange situation |
Investigator	Population	Age	Strange situation		
Causey	6 beagles	7 weeks	strange room	260	920
Ross *et al.*	6 cockers 17 hybrids	3–6 weeks	small cage, home pen	569*	1493*
Bronson	6 beagles	7–8 weeks	large cage, home pen	869	1206
Elliot and Scott	8 beagles	6 weeks	strange room	430	1410

* Based on 2 different groups of pups.

Bronson has also tested the interaction of hunger with isolation. Six beagle puppies were fed at 9 A.M. each day for 10 days, so that they became accustomed to eating only at this hour. Yelps were counted, either before or after their 9 A.M. feeding, in one of three situations: together in their home pen, isolated in their home pen, or isolated in a strange cage in their home pen. From a baseline of 52 yelps per pup over a 10-minute period when the pups were together and not hungry, the mean yelp count rose by a factor of five when they were together and hungry and, ultimately, by a factor of approximately 24 when the pups were isolated in a strange cage, re- gardless of whether they were hungry or not (see Table 4). Isolation in their home pen produced a 17-fold increase in yelps compared with the baseline. It is obvious from Table 4 that, while hunger in- creased vocalization when the pups were neither isolated nor in a strange situation, the effect of hunger was lost when either or both of these two latter factors were operating on the pup. We can con- clude that the emotions generated by them suppress that of hunger.

TABLE 4

*Effects of Combining Isolation, and Isolation in a
Strange Situation, with Hunger*

	Mean vocalization rates per 10 minutes	
	Before feeding (hungry)	After feeding (satiated)
Together, home pen	264	52
Isolated, home pen	883	869
Isolated, strange cage	1249	1206

Thus, the emotions produced by isolation and strangeness are com- patible and additive in nature, but both are incompatible with hunger. This raises the question of the nature of the emotion that the puppies are experiencing during isolation.

Experiments on the Nature of the Emotion. Puppies appear to be lonely and afraid when isolated in a strange situation, but one can- not ask them how they feel. Even if they could talk, they might be like human beings, who are often unable to describe their emotions accurately. One way to get at the nature of their emotional responses will be to measure the physiological responses of the puppies with telemetering devices, and we hope to do this in the future. Another method is to take common drugs that have well-authenticated effects upon human emotional states and apply them to the puppy. If the results are similar, we have one line of evidence that the emotions are similar.

In a preliminary study (Scott and Bronson, 1962) we chose chlorpromazine, which is effective in the reduction of anxiety in human subjects, and amphetamine, which in addition to its direct physiological effects of raising blood pressure and reducing gastrointestinal motility, is reported to produce a feeling of euphoria. We hypothesized that both these drugs should reduce the yelping rate, and this was indeed the case (see Table 5). One curious finding was that the two drugs did not produce an additive effect, the combination giving the same result as either one alone. These preliminary experiments were done on a group of older dogs in which the distress vocalization rate was rapidly declining. The results are therefore tentative, but are consistent with the assumption that the emotion is one related to fear or loneliness.

TABLE 5

*Effect of Chlorpromazine and Benzedrine on Vocalization Rates
of Puppies Aged 3½ to 5½ Months**

| Drug | Mean rate per minute | | Decrease (%) |
	Control	Drug	
Chlorpromazine	85.8	27.0	69‡
	47.0	28.4	40†
Benzedrine	49.4	22.9	54‡
	26.1	18.1	31
Chlorpromazine and	88.2	57.9	34‡
Benzedrine	26.8	16.9	37

* Dosage rates = 6.5 mg per K and 0.4 mg per K. Tests were made under two conditions: high and low response levels. Consistent results appeared at both levels, but were statistically meaningful only at the higher rates.
† $p = .01$, Wilcoxon test.
‡ $p = .005$.

Effects of Emotional Disturbance on Later Behavior. The strong emotional response of young puppies to isolation in a strange place provides an opportunity for studying the effects of a potentially traumatic emotional experience. In an experiment to be reported elsewhere (Scott, Deshaies, and Morris, 1963) we separated puppies from their mothers overnight during the critical period for socialization. Each puppy had this experience eight times between the ages of 5 and 7 weeks. The chief result was to speed up the process of primary socialization to a human handler as measured by both a decrease of fear and avoidance reactions and a decrease in the running time toward the handler. Control litter mates given similar treatment and handling, except for isolation, lagged behind considerably. Another immediate effect of the experience was that the puppies lost weight, even though large amounts of food were provided in the isolation box. Puppies weaned at this age and kept in groups may lose weight for the first few days, but usually fare better than unweaned puppies, because of now having access to an unlimited food supply. These experimental animals, however, suffered serious losses in weight, which were not made up until after they were restored to their litters. This again supports the conclusion that the emotion induced by isolation in a strange place is incompatible with that of hunger.

These same puppies were studied until they were 6 months old, and their behavior was measured in a variety of test situations. For the most part, the differences produced by the emotional experience rapidly disappeared, and only one of them persisted strongly. The behavior of Shetland sheep dogs that were trained to sit immediately after the experience was permanently affected, the experimental animals being unable to remain still as long as controls. They retained some of the nervous and agitated behavior they had shown when first taught. The experiment indicates that the emotional experience affected only behavior being learned at the time. We have no results on the effects of more drastic types of isolation experience, but it would be expected that the puppies would not recover so completely and that more of their behavior might be permanently affected. The experiment leads to one hopeful conclusion—that these young animals have considerable capacity to recover from a relatively drastic emotional experience early in their lives, provided that they are immediately restored to normal conditions.

Genetic Differences. There are obvious breed differences in the reactions of neonatal puppies to the discomfort of being weighed (Scott, 1957b). Basenjis, while relatively non-vocal in later life, show considerably higher rates of vocalization at birth than the rest of the breeds, and beagles show lower ones. Presumably, most of the discomfort is caused by contact with the cold platform of the scale, and the results are consistent with this assumption, basenjis having short coats and beagles having longer hair and a thicker coating of fat.

We have thoroughly studied the development of distress vocalization in reaction to isolation in a strange place in only one breed, the beagle (Elliot and Scott, 1961), but are now accumulating data on a second. At 3 and 4 weeks of age cocker spaniels show a higher rate of vocalization than beagles, but the rate for both begins to decline at approximately the same point, after reaching a peak at 6 to 7 weeks of age (see Fig. 1.).

We also have comparative data on 5- to 7-week-old basenjis and shelties isolated in strange cages (Scott, Deshaies, and Morris, 1963). Vocalization rates of the shelties are approximately three times those of the basenjis. Thus there are indications of important differences between breeds as well as of variations among individuals. These

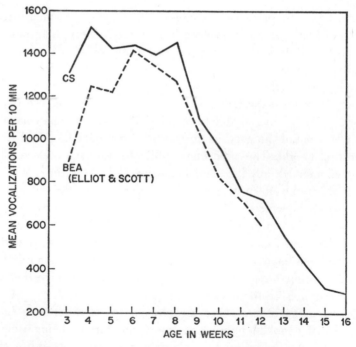

Fig. 1. Effect of heredity upon vocalization rate. The figure represents the results of comparing two populations of eight animals each, in different experiments.

genetic differences may simply reflect differences in the capacity to vocalize. It seems more likely, however, that they represent differences in the level of emotional arousal; i.e., a situation that is highly disturbing to one individual may be only moderately so to another.

We conclude that there is a particular and identifiable emotional reaction in puppies associated with social isolation in a strange place, that this is expressed along with certain other emotions as distress vocalization, and that these reactions are organized into a behavioral system characteristic of young animals. We can now consider the significance of these findings in relation to a general theoretical framework.

The Systematics of Social Behavior

A system may be defined as an organized group of entities, and the following systems are attempts to represent the organization of natural phenomena. All of them are strongly relevent to behavior. To use a spatial analogy, they may be thought of as three independent dimensions measuring the universe of social behavior, and they may be used together to locate any particular behavioral phenomenon in relation to the rest.

The Linnaean System of Taxonomy. One of the first naturally occurring systems recognized by biologists was the grand scheme of plant and animal classification based on fundamental similarities attributable to common origins and genetic relationships. Therefore, in approaching any problem of social behavior the first question to ask is, "What species is exhibiting the behavior and where does it belong in the animal kingdom?" The answer to this question limits generalization. It is well to remember that generality of any fact or theory concerning social behavior can be established only by examining a broad sample of such behavior in various parts of the animal kingdom. One of the major functions of the animal behaviorist trained in biology is to establish this sort of generality. It is only when we know that a phenomenon occurs widely in the animal kingdom that we are justified in assuming that it is likely also to be found in man and that it has basic importance.

With respect to this system, we have in these experiments analyzed some of the behavior of dogs, belonging to the species *Canis familiaris*, Family Canidae, Order Carnivora, and Class Mammalia. Dogs belong to a different order from men, but their behavior is of particular interest to human beings because dogs are the oldest domestic animals and, as such, have been a part of human society for thousands of years. Many of the behavior patterns of the two species are mutually comprehensible, and puppies develop with their human masters a social relationship that is in many ways comparable to the human parent-child relationship.

Levels of Organization. As Table 6 shows, biological phenomena are organized on many levels. Behavior is the primary phenomenon in which we are interested, and to study it we can go back to the lower levels of physiology and genetics to search for basic causes, we can stay on the level of individual organization, as most psychologists do, or we can look for causes of behavior on the higher levels of sociology and ecology. In the latter instances we must recognize that factors on the higher levels have some effect on organization on lower levels, as well as the other way around.

TABLE 6

Major Levels of Organization in Relation to the Study of Behavior

Level	Major units of organization	
Ecological	Communities, Populations ↓	
Social	Societies, Social Groups ↓	
Organismic	Organisms	⟶ BEHAVIOR
	↑	
Physiological	Organ Systems, Organs, Cells ↑	
Genetic (Molecular)	Genes, Molecules	

It is obvious that the levels of organization correspond to the conventional territories of some of the older scientific disciplines, but that one of these older approaches, that of development, cuts across many of them. As an organism grows and matures it passes through and becomes associated with all levels of organization.

Reference to this system answers the experimenter's question, "On what level of organization am I working with respect to the various possible causes of behavior?" and indicates to him the variety of other factors that he must keep under control. The data reported here have been collected from a developmental approach that has cut across the genetic, organismic, and social levels of organization. In working with emotional causes of behavior, we are inferring phenomena on the physiological level also, and we are preparing to examine these more directly in the future.

Systems of Behavior. Each animal species has certain methods of adaptation that are peculiar to it. These characteristic patterns of behavior are not inherited as such but must be developed. Their development is guided and limited by the anatomy and physiology of the species and the fundamental organization of the nervous system, is modified by environmental stimulation, and is finally organized under the combined influence of all these factors plus the process of learning.

A *behavior pattern* may be defined as a unit of behavior having a special function. Each species usually has several alternative behavior patterns for any one function. For example, a mouse attacked by another mouse may either fight back, assume a defensive posture, run away, or simply freeze and become immobile. An inexperienced mouse will usually try them out in turn. All of these behavior patterns have the same general function—adaptation to physical conflict— and we can speak of them collectively as a *behavioral system,* a group of behavior patterns organized in part by the heredity of the species but also by the process of learning. A behavioral system exists partly on the physiological level and partly on the organismic level. The group of behavior patterns organized for adaptation to physical conflict forms the agonistic behavioral system (see Table 7).

We can think of the behavior pattern as the functional unit of

TABLE 7

Areas Where Extensive Research Has Been Done on Basic Causes of Social Behavior

Behavioral system	Genetic	Physio- logical	Psycho- logical	Social	Eco- logical	Develop- mental
Ingestive		x	x			?
Investigative			?			
Shelter-seeking					x	
Sexual	?	x				
Epimeletic						
Et-epimeletic						
Allelomimetic						
Agonistic	x	x	?	x		x
Eliminative						

? designates areas where less comprehensive research has been done.

behavior. In understanding the social behavior of any species it is therefore necessary to make an inventory of the behavioral repertoire of the species, consisting of a description of the various patterns of behavior exhibited by its members. Tinbergen (1951) has called such an inventory the *ethogram*. The further organization of the ethogram into behavioral systems and higher levels of organization must be determined by observation and experiment. In any given individual, behavior patterns are organized into systems of behavior, and these in turn are organized between individuals into social relationships. Social groups may be organized into populations, and populations in turn into animal communities.

The behavior that we have analyzed in this chapter belongs to the et-epimeletic or care-soliciting system of behavior. In the dog, this system has two functions. One of these is to make positive social contacts through tail wagging and social investigation. The other function is adaptation to certain situations that are beyond the capacity of the puppy, and this is accomplished through distress vocalization. These two patterns of behavior are comparable in the human infant to smiling and visual investigation on the one hand, and crying on the other. Compared with the great variety of adult methods of adaptation, the et-epimeletic system is expressed in a few simple patterns of behavior.

As the puppies grow older the rate of vocalization in isolation declines rapidly. This may be taken as an indication of the decline of the et-epimeletic system of behavior. An older dog confined in isolation will usually sit down and wait to be let out, or try to tear the confining cage to pieces, instead of constantly yelping. While it lasts, however, this system of behavior is an extraordinarily interesting one which provides numerous research opportunities. One obvious fact is that the curve of vocalization follows very closely the curve for the development and decline of the capacity for rapid primary socialization, and we have suggested elsewhere that socialization is dependent upon emotional arousal (Scott, 1962).

Distress vocalization is the infant animal's first means of dealing with problems of difficult adaptation. Later it is supplanted by other and more direct methods of adaptation, so that the function of the et-epimeletic behavioral system becomes subdivided among other systems, particularly those of shelter- or comfort-seeking behavior, ingestive behavior, and agonistic behavior. An unexpected result of this study is the indication that allelomimetic behavior is also involved. Isolation in the puppy produces an emotion which is uncomfortable and which is immediately relieved by the presence of other animals. A young animal would be expected to learn quickly that in order to avoid such emotions he must do as the others do, and this could lead to a very strong habit of running in packs, whether canine or human. This suggests that the emotional response to isolation may function as a general motivational basis for maintaining social contact.

On the other hand, distress vocalization has no important function as a substitute for sexual behavior, epimeletic or care-giving behavior, investigative behavior, or eliminative behavior. The first two of these are not important problems in infantile life. Investigation is more closely related to tail wagging, and eliminative behavior ordinarily requires no help.

Distress vocalization tends to disappear in older dogs, being reduced to a low level by 4 months of age. An adult animal still has the capacity for distress vocalization, but is likely to employ it only briefly if at all. In human beings crying is likewise possible for adults but is greatly reduced in frequency. The human being, however, has the possibility of using language to ask for help. This fact suggests the hypothesis that verbal solutions to problems, particularly in the form of asking for help and assistance, may be most effective with respect to those behavioral systems for which distress vocalization is normally employed in infantile life.

Systematic Search for the Causes of Behavior. The systematic approach to behavior can be used to locate research problems and neglected areas of investigation. As seen in Table 7, there are some nine important behavioral systems. The first four of these are found very widely in the animal kingdom, and examples can be found even in the one-celled animals. The last five are behavioral systems which are characteristic of the higher animals, particularly vertebrates and arthropods, although some indications of them may also be seen in the most highly developed mollusks.

In the table we have indicated the points where we have some extensive knowledge of each behavioral system on various levels of organization. On the genetic level, although there is a great deal of information regarding species differences in behavior, detailed studies of actual inheritance have been made only with agonistic behavior and to a lesser extent with sexual behavior. We are referring here to crosses made between strains, or between closely related species, in which careful measurements of behavior have been made.

With regard to the physiological causes of behavior, we know a great deal about the physiology of ingestive behavior in many different species of animals, and we are rapidly accumulating information on the physiology of sexual behavior. The physiology of agonistic behavior has been thoroughly explored in only one species, the domestic cat.

On the organismic or psychological level, the effect of learning upon behavior has been thoroughly studied in relation to only one system, ingestive behavior, and we would estimate that 95 per cent of all experiments on learning involve this one type of behavior. The rest chiefly concern the reactions of an animal to the pain of electric shock, which probably belongs to the system of agonistic behavior. The task of establishing Pavlovian principles of learning as broad general laws affecting all kinds of social behavior is still largely to be done, and we may anticipate that in the future many new discoveries will come from this.

On the level of social organization, only one system of behavior has been widely studied, that of agonistic behavior. In spite of their fundamental importance, other kinds of social relationships such as care-dependency, mutual care, and leadership have been little studied.

On the ecological level, the relationship between the environment and the formation of aggregations through shelter-seeking behavior was established as a broad general phenomenon by the late W. C. Allee (1931), and we have many current studies that involve the effects of population density upon reproduction.

Finally, we would hesitate to say that thorough developmental studies have been made of any system of social behavior. We have just begun to scratch the surface of this field, and this chapter reports the results of such a pioneering study. In general, the most striking thing about Table 7 is the enormous blank space that remains to be filled in. There are four major systems of behavior which are as yet almost completely unknown.

Another point which follows from this table is that any attempt to analyze the causes of a particular system of behavior will inevitably produce some sort of multiple-factor theory. Causal factors exist on every level of organization and, as one of us has pointed out elsewhere (Scott, 1957a), many of the apparent contradictions between different schools of psychology and psychiatry result from concentration of research upon causes at only one level of organization, to the neglect of others. The existence of multiple behavioral systems as well as multiple causal factors affecting them further implies that it is no longer fruitful to interpret behavior in terms of dichotomous categories and bipolar concepts. Because sexual and agonistic behavior are the two systems most likely to be suppressed and distorted by human culture, clinicians have tended to set up motivational schemes that include only these two. Obviously there is a great deal more to behavior than this.

Systematic Approach to Clinical Problems. We have so far used the combined concepts of biological relationships, levels of organization, and behavioral systems as a method of locating and evaluating research problems, but the same scheme can also be applied to the problems of clinical practice. The clinician's position is somewhat like that of a detective who is presented with a crime and asked to name the criminal or gang of criminals who committed it. To be truly scientific we must search for the causes of a clinical phenomenon in a systematic way. We must first ask, "What fundamental system or systems of behavior are disturbed?" When this question is answered, the next step is to examine each level of organization in turn for possible causes, beginning on the genetic level and proceeding through physiological, psychological, social, and ecological phenomena. Frequently a patient will have more than one set of factors disturbing his behavior, and the choice of what the clinician may recommend will depend upon practical considerations. For example, the fundamental cause might lie in the social environment. In the case of a child, the clinician may be able to recommend to the parents a course of action that will change the social milieu. Alternatively, a solution on the physiological level may be sufficient to allow the patient to cope with his social difficulties.

In the case of many adults, the clinician may be unable to change the patient's social environment and so must help the patient change himself or his circumstances. Thus the patient adapts to what cannot be changed by the physician, either by changing himself or by changing his environment.

Conclusion

This chapter presents a broad and general psychobiological approach to social behavior, ideally involving all behavioral systems considered on every level of social organization and compared among a large number of animal species. Most of the other studies reported in this book are more specific, being concerned chiefly with the agonistic system of behavior and its physiological causes and effects within the human species. In our own work we have likewise been specific, but have presented data on the dog, a mammal distantly related to man, and have reported exploratory studies on different levels of organization of a system of behavior which is most prominent in early development and which, in fact, largely serves as a substitute for several more slowly developing systems. This work has led into several new problems, but the most important result is the discovery of what appears to be a primary motivational mechanism which is related to the allelomimetic behavioral system and which may function as a general social drive. The physiology of this mechanism that can so far be inferred is different from that in ingestive behavior, but is somewhat related to the motivational basis of agonistic behavior, in that an emotion akin to fear or loneliness is involved. This emotion can be immediately aroused in young puppies by social isolation in a strange environment, and has the adaptive function of keeping young animals together in familiar places, a reaction which would provide maximum safety in a wild species. The infant animals soon learn that it is pleasant to stay with the group and unpleasant to be alone, which leads to the development of strong general social motivation. From observational evidence it is possible that such a mechanism may also exist in human development and, if so, it should be investigated.

We have reported here the current results of a systematic attempt to collect basic information regarding one of the major behavioral systems of infantile existence. Much of this work has consisted of the slow and unglamorous collection of facts, but it has its rewarding aspects in the suggestion of new insights and ideas. In the long run, the ideas may be tested by experiment and confirmed or found wanting, but the facts will remain as the basis for wider generalizations.

REFERENCES

Allee, W. C. *Animal aggregations.* Chicago: Univ. of Chicago Press, 1931.

Causey, Anne. A developmental study of emotionality in puppies under conditions of stress. (Unpublished Ms., Bar Harbor, Me.: The Jackson Laboratory, 1956.)

Elliot, O., and Scott, J. P. The development of emotional distress reactions to separation, in puppies. *J. genet. Psychol.,* 1961, 99, 3–22.

Fredericson, E. Distributed versus massed experience in a traumatic situation. *J. abnorm. soc. Psychol.,* 1950, **45,** 259–66.

Fredericson, E. Perceptual homeostasis and distress vocalization in puppies. *J. Pers.,* 1952, **20,** 472–77.

Gewirtz, J. L. Changes in the course of human smiling through the first 18 months of life. Second Tavistock Study Group on Mother-Infant Interacaction, Bethesda, Md. (mimeographed by author), 1961.

Ross, S., Scott, J. P., Cherner, M., and Denenberg, V. H. Effects of restraint and isolation on yelping in puppies. *Anim. Behav.,* 1960, 8, 1–5.

Scott, J. P. Comment on the psychosocial position. In H. D. Kruse (Ed.), *Integrating the approaches to mental disease,* New York: Hoeber-Harper, 1957a. Pp. 154–59.

Scott, J. P. The genetic and environmental differentiation of behavior. In D. B. Harris (Ed.), *The concept of development,* Minneapolis: Univ. of Minn. Press, 1957b. Pp. 59–77.

Scott, J. P. Critical periods in behavioral development, *Science,* 1962, **138,** 949–58.

Scott, J. P., and Bronson, F. H. Modification of distress vocalization of puppies by drugs. 3rd Ann. Meeting Psychonomic Society, 1962, p. 41.

Scott, J. P., Fredericson, E., and Fuller, J. L. Experimental exploration of the critical period hypothesis. *Personality,* 1951, 1, 162–83.

Scott, J. P., Deshaies, D., and Morris, D. D. The effect of emotional arousal on primary socialization in the dog. (Unpublished Ms., Bar Harbor, Me.: The Jackson Laboratory, 1963.)

Tinbergen, N. *The study of instinct.* Oxford: Oxford Univ. Press, 1951.

Implications *by the Editors*

The wide range of methods of study and the variety of concepts employed in these papers reveal a viable and creative research area. Clearly, the work reported in this volume has many implications for future research. Probably the most fundamental contribution is the suggestion of a methodological and conceptual framework for a fruitful exchange between the psychobiological and the social sciences.

Apart from the substantive contributions, one major accomplishment of these papers is their description of various combinations of methods for relating social influences and physiological response. Presumably, as biological and biochemical techniques develop beyond their present level of refinement, they will have even greater applicability to research in experimental social psychology. Perhaps more fundamental than the use of these biological methods is the introduction of suitable mathematical techniques. One example of the need for such techniques is the absence of time series analysis for time-ordered data in the studies in this volume. The application of these techniques will be an important part of psychophysiology and behavioral research in the future.

Turning now to the substantive contributions of these papers, we find a number of possibilities for future research. A promising direction is provided by those studies which attempt to manipulate social variables, either in the ongoing situation (e.g., Shapiro and Leiderman) or by pre-experimental selection and arrangement of individuals (e.g., Kaplan, Burch, and Bloom; Back and Bogdonoff). Small groups of two, three, and four subjects could be studied under the varying effects of social approval and disapproval, success and failure, cooperation and competition, formal and informal social settings, conditions of isolation, and varying social relationships. Groups selected for personality type, patient category, occupational group, sex, and ethnicity could be evaluated in these different social environments. Such studies might yield a taxonomy of group behavior based on behavioral-physiological relationships.

Another direction supplied by the findings is the study of the socialization of physiological response levels during the course of maturation. If group factors are as significant an influence on physiological response levels as the studies in this book imply, physiological studies of family interaction during the course of development could provide very useful information concerning the individual and family structure. The work of Scott and Bronson indicates the possibilities for similar types of study in infra-human organisms. Some questions that might be raised are: What are the mechanisms of social-physiological learning? What are the relative importances of constitutional and environmental influences in family interaction? To what extent are individually consistent and habitual modes of physiological expression conditioned by social influences? Are these early influences related to subsequent development of psychosomatic illness? These psychophysiological studies might well begin with the interaction between mother and infant and proceed longitudinally throughout development.

The physiological concomitants of group formation constitute another intriguing area. The paper by Mason and Brady develops the concept of physiological convergence. Their work shows that the group influences a physiological response system by bringing responses toward an intermediate level. This finding for a biological variable may be compared to the mutual identification process often noted in groups. Similarly, Kaplan, Burch, and Bloom in their work suggest that a mutual relationship, depending on its affective definition, may result in a covarying physiological response pattern, a kind of physiological empathy. These observations raise many possibilities for research. What are the social and biological mechanisms that account for these regularities in a group setting? What is the function of a common physical environment? A shared social environment? Are there physiological counterparts to "becoming a group"?

The general problem of physiological and behavioral relationships remains unsettled. Several papers (Horwitz, Glass, and Niyekawa; Shapiro and Leiderman; Gerard) in this book emphasize the complexity of these relationships, showing that there is no simple relationship between skeletal, autonomic, and behavioral activity. Perhaps the confounding of results in previous studies can be attributed to lack of control of social variables. A similar argument might be made for endocrine and autonomic interrelationships (see Mason and Brady). In future psychophysiological research, the specification of social variables will have to be made as precise as it is for physical variables.

The papers of Back and Bogdonoff; Kaplan, Burch, and Bloom; and Shapiro and Leiderman show that the same social conditions can affect autonomic, endocrine, and behavioral response in different ways. For example, the direction of change of behavior, whether increase or decrease, can be relatively independent of the direction of change of physiological response levels. On occasions the two systems are linked quite closely. Basic studies are needed on the processes of behavioral and physiological variation under different types of social facilitation. Are well-learned habits characterized by low levels of physiological response? Further clues to the answer to this question might be found in the study of patients with well-defined activity patterns, such as compulsive motor behaviors, catatonia, hypomanic activity, depressed activity, consistent states of withdrawal, or apathy. The question could be posed, To what extent can situational influences modify these consistent modes of behavioral and physiological response?

The degree to which visceral responses can be learned or unlearned under different conditions of social reward has important implications for psychosomatic medicine (see Horwitz, Glass, and Niyekawa). In effect we need to expand our usual conceptions of mind-body relationships to include the learning that can take place under varying social and group circumstances. Sociosomatic concepts must take their rightful place with psychosomatic concepts in psychiatric thinking.

The relationship between cognitive and other subjective states, and bodily states such as autonomic and endocrine levels needs to be studied more fully. Gerard's paper indicates that subtle combinations of attitude, conviction, and commitment have different consequences for physiological arousal. Schachter's work makes it clear that situational factors provide a structure on which an individual's interpretation of his bodily states is built. At present little is known about the interaction between physiological states and cognitive processes. Such interaction could be investigated by monitoring physiological variables before, during, and after manipulating social and cognitive stimuli, thereby approaching the quantification of tension and arousal states directly.

The relationship between pharmacological agents and social behavior is almost unexplored. Lennard emphasizes the way in which group behavior can be utilized more directly in psychopharmacological research. A social situation is the only appropriate testing ground for assessing the value of a drug in influencing an individual's adaptation to his social environment. Unless the effects of drugs, such as tranquilizers and anti-depressants, are studied in a variety of social situations, it is difficult to make suitable generalizations about their value for the individual who is perforce embedded in the social environment. The effect of drugs on social systems should be as carefully specified as it has been on physiological and behavioral systems.

One of the fundamental problems facing those who study biological and social phenomena lies in relating events from dissimilar conceptual levels. It is obvious that the relationship of the individual to his environment, which is the focus of social psychology, cannot be reduced to internal physiological functioning. It is equally apparent that the intricacies of physiological processes cannot be easily placed in psychological categories. To take these considerations into account, better theories of social behavior on the biological as well as on the social level will be required. Research dealing with single conceptual levels may provide the basis for a synthesis of concepts derived from many levels. Whether the combination of different levels of analysis in the study of social behavior in itself will lead to new theories of human behavior cannot yet be known. We believe that the concrete data obtained in a psychobiological framework will require a revision of present concepts of the individual in group interaction. These findings, along with informed guessing, refined observation, and close logic may lead us to a breakthrough toward a more comprehensive theory of human behavior.

Index